The Mathematical Murder
of Innocence

The
Mathematical
Murder
of
Innocence

INSPIRED BY A TRUE STORY

Michael Carter

The Book Guild Ltd

First published in Great Britain in 2020 by
The Book Guild Ltd
9 Priory Business Park
Wistow Road, Kibworth
Leicestershire, LE8 0RX
Freephone: 0800 999 2982
www.bookguild.co.uk
Email: info@bookguild.co.uk
Twitter: @bookguild

Typeset in Adobe Garamond Pro

Printed on FSC accredited paper
Printed and bound in Great Britain by 4edge Limited

ISBN 978 191355 102 5

British Library Cataloguing in Publication Data.
A catalogue record for this book is available from the British Library.

Author's note

I have set this story today; but it is an idea that has been in my mind for some years.

It is inspired by true events from 1998-2003. There were many newspaper articles about how a mother had at last been acquitted on her second appeal for the double murder of her baby sons. At her original trial an 'expert' witness had convinced the jury to convict her due to his incorrect statistical analysis of the probability of double cot deaths. When I read the details, I was outraged. I told myself that anyone with a basic maths education could have seen through this assassination of statistics. Yet nobody did, at the time. Then I thought to myself, if I had been there, at the trial, maybe as a juror, what could I have done...?

This story is largely fiction, but many of the arguments used by the prosecution are taken both from this true landmark trial, as well as from a very similar, and parallel, miscarriage of justice due to testimony from the same expert witness about another case of double cot deaths. Just about every argument used to defend against the prosecution is also true, except in real life they took a lot longer to come out. Too long.

Prologue

It was 8pm when the street doorbell rang. Daniel pushed the intercom. "Hello?"

"Metropolitan Police here, sir. Is Sarah Richardson there?"

"Yes, she is. What can she do for you?"

"Can we just come in, please, sir?"

"OK, first floor." Daniel pushed the buzzer to open the street door.

"Darling, the police want you! You been cooking your clients' books or something?"

Sarah gave a weak smile. It was good that Daniel kept a sense of humour despite the weight of their tragedies. They heard the footsteps coming up the stairs, and then the flat's inner doorbell rang.

Daniel opened the door. "Good evening, officers. Please come in. What's up?"

Two men entered, one in plain clothes and the other a constable in uniform. Plain clothes spoke, turning to

Sarah, who had come out onto the landing. "Mrs Sarah Richardson?"

"Yes," she replied, "that's me."

"I am D.S. Tooley and this is Constable Harris. I have to inform you that you are under arrest for the murder of your son George. You do not have to say anything. But it may harm your defence if you do not mention when questioned something which you later rely on in court. Anything you do say may be given in evidence."

Sarah collapsed, sobbing and bewildered, into her husband's arms.

An hour later they were at Clapham police station. Sarah hadn't stopped sobbing all the way there in the Dacia police car. Despite her shock, in the back of her consultant's brain she still registered her analysis about how budget cuts must be cutting into the Metropolitan Police. A Dacia?

D.S. Tooley started the recording in the interview room. He stated his rank, name, the date and time, and the persons present. "You are entitled to have a lawyer present, ma'am. Would you like to call one?" he asked.

"I don't need a lawyer!" cried Sarah. "It's obvious I didn't do this; how can you accuse me, a mother, of murdering my own babies? You've made some enormous mistake."

"Then please take us over the events of April 14th last, ma'am," said Tooley.

An innocent person does not need a lawyer, or so they think. This is a mistake. If the police are convinced that the person is guilty, they might take any single statement out of context to support their narrative; and they might be convinced they are right. No person charged with a crime, even if innocent, should talk to the police without first having gone through their story with a criminal lawyer, and to have that lawyer present for all questioning.

There is a risk that refusing to talk without a lawyer might give the impression of guilt. But to avoid miscarriages of justice it is the least bad decision to take.

For Sarah, that evening was indelibly engraved in her memory, as she took the police through what had happened.

She had got back to her Battersea flat at 7pm. The tube to Waterloo had been bad enough, but the crush on the overground to Clapham Junction had been a real nightmare. She'd had ten minutes' walk to clear her head and breathe in the mixture of cool night air and car fumes from the station to her flat, to reflect on whether she really was doing the right thing by being a mother of a young child, while keeping her career as a junior management consultant in one of the big four accountancy firms. Most of her university friends took the micky out of her for becoming an accountant, although she explained as often as she could that what she did – consulting in strategy, marketing and operations to different business clients in the consumer goods sector – was very different from financial auditing. Or was it? Was she wasting her Oxford degree with what she was doing? Or was she trying to prove to herself that she was as good as her degree suggested and wasting her time as a young mother? She needed both, she concluded. Above all, after what had happened two years ago...

She had unlocked the outside door and climbed the steps two at a time to her first floor flat in the three-storey house, dating to when in the 1930s they had built this suburb north of Clapham Common. She desperately wanted to see her little George. As she opened her front door she called out: "Julia, I'm home."

Her Polish au pair came out of the kitchen. "Evening, Sarah," she said. "George has finished his bottle, I changed his nappy, and he seems to have settled down to sleep."

"On his back?" asked Sarah.

"Of course!" replied Julia. There was no question of his being allowed to sleep on his tummy, not after what happened last time.

Sarah gently opened the door to the baby's room and went up to the cot. George seemed to sense her presence and wiggled slightly in his sleep, before peacefully continuing his dreams.

"He looks so content," she said. "Are you eating in tonight?"

"No," replied Julia, "I'm meeting a couple of girlfriends down the pub, and we'll probably grab a curry afterwards. When in Rome, do as the Romans do… you English with your beer and your national dish of Indian curry…! I'll be off if you don't need me?"

"Off you go," encouraged Sarah. "Daniel is dining out with clients, so I'll just microwave something from the freezer."

One hour later, having eaten an aubergine gratin, she decided to check up on George. She opened the door and crept up on him. He seemed so peaceful. So very peaceful. Too peaceful. She stroked his cheek. There was no reaction, no movement. A slow but clear feeling of panic began to take hold in the pit of Sarah's stomach. No! Don't be silly. He's just in a deep sleep. Sarah rushed to turn on the main light. There was no sign of breathing. No, she must be imagining it. She picked him up. No sign at all. He wasn't that warm either, not cold, but not the usual feeling of heat coming from his smooth skin.

"Don't do this to me, darling!" she cried. She tried to feel for a pulse on his little wrist, but she had always found this difficult to find even on herself, let alone on a baby. She couldn't find it. So, she tried to the side under the chin. Still nothing. "No! No!" she was screaming. The panic had really set in. He's not breathing! She laid him on the floor and started mouth-to-mouth resuscitation. One then two breaths. Then she pushed hard down on his chest as she remembered from her Duke of Edinburgh community service courses in first aid. Except that all those exercises had been on a dummy of a grown adult; so, she tried to scale everything down to this four-week-old baby. One, two, three, four... all the way up to thirty pushes onto his little breastbone, at almost two a second, pushing down as hard as she dared. 'Better a broken breastbone than a dead person,' they had said. She then followed this by two more breaths over the little mouth, and repeated the cycle over and over.

It wasn't working. Not again! Not again! Why my baby? Why me? Oh, George, come back to me! Come back. After twenty minutes of frantic effort, she just collapsed onto the floor sobbing her heart out. He was dead.

She groped for her phone in her handbag in the hall. She went to her recently dialled phone list and tapped on Daniel's number. After three rings he answered. "Hi, Sarah. We're just finishing dinner here. What's up?"

"It's George. He's dead. He's dead, Daniel! I can't resuscitate him. It's happened again!"

It was plain clothes again. The Tooley guy. "Why didn't you first call 999 for an ambulance, Mrs Richardson? Why was your first call to your husband?"

"Because I knew he was dead. I knew even before I tried the resuscitation. But I had to try."

"Are you sure that's the real story, Mrs Richardson? Perhaps you knew he was dead for another reason. Because it was you who had killed him."

"How can you accuse me of that? It was my baby. Our baby. The one we had so longed for. The one we already had once, but then lost him too. We're just cursed!"

"I have to inform you that we've looked into the results of the autopsy," continued Tooley. "They include a possibility of death by deliberate smothering and suffocation. It would be much better for you to come clean, love. We all know what it's like to have small children. I'd have smothered my blighters several times given half a chance!"

Sarah just stared at him, shaking her head.

There was a knock on the door. The desk officer put his head round. "A Mr Richardson has just arrived. In quite a state. He's double parked his BMW outside the station."

"Better show him in then, put him in room 2 and I'll talk to him separately later," said Tooley. "Take his keys and put the car around the back. Looks like we're in for a long night."

Tooley turned back to Sarah. "Take us through the challenges of having a career and of being a young mother," he said.

Chapter One

How had I got myself into this position? Why couldn't I keep my mouth shut? But no, I could not stand idly by while one of the most erudite expert witnesses assassinated basic mathematics in order to accuse a mother of murder.

Standing up in the jury box, I very nervously cleared my throat. I looked around me. If looks could kill, I was already dead under the triple assault of the two prosecution barristers' and the expert witness' scowls. The judge was looking at me expectantly; the lead defence counsel had a hopeful look of invitation; the defendant was searching my face with pleading eyes. Many of the people in court seemed to have an expression of genuine curiosity, they were witnessing a legal precedent in real time – the judge had invited a member of the jury to cross examine a key witness! Doubtless he did this just to shut me up, but you could feel their unspoken question: whatever could this young jury member possibly say to challenge such an erudite expert witness? And what on earth did the judge think he was doing?

With all eyes looking at me, I stammered out my first question. "Pr-Professor Goodwin, you say that there is only a one in seventy-two million chance that Mrs Richardson's children died of natural causes?"

"Yes, that is exactly what I said. Very clearly and several times."

"So, if I am to understand from your statement," I continued a little more confidently, "the defendant was chosen purely at random, pulled in off the street if you like, and *only then* was it discovered that two of her babies had died in succession?"

"Don't be ridiculous, young man!" retorted Goodwin. "We all know Mrs Richardson was arrested for murder precisely because her baby boys had died."

"I agree with the witness, my Lord," said the prosecution. "This is ridiculous. Must we really go on?"

"Mr Fielding," interrupted the judge, "please get to the point and do not treat the court to facetious remarks."

"My Lord. From a mathematical point of view, Professor Goodwin's statement is exactly as if she *were* pulled in off the street at random," I replied.

"Well, you had better get on with it and explain yourself, then."

"Professor, please explain again how you reached your calculation."

"I repeat, *again*: there is a one in 8,500 chance of the first death being a cot death, multiplied by one in 8,500 for the second, thus one in 72 million. Statistically impossible to happen by accident. It had to be murder."

"But how many births are there in the UK every year?" I asked.

"About 800,000," he replied.

I was beginning to enjoy this. "So, within a time frame of, say, ten years – since fortunately we don't often hear about double baby murders – we could, conceptually, have pulled in from the streets ten times 800,000, that's 8 million women, who have recently given birth. Let's say half of them, 4 million, had had second or third births. Then we ask them if two of their babies had died in a row? And yes, it so happens that one of them, Mrs Richardson, fits that profile. My point is that we had 4 million different chances to find someone guilty. So, Professor Goodwin, your probability is not one in 72 million, it's one in 72 million divided by 4 million which is exactly one in eighteen. Not one in eighteen hundred or one in eighteen thousand, but one in eighteen!"

And I had hardly started to dismantle his arguments...

My name is Martin Fielding. It had all started when I received a summons for jury duty. Normally jury duty is for two weeks, but I was advised to reserve a three-to-four-week period starting mid-November. I discussed it with my HR manager and with my immediate boss at work. They were not particularly pleased about this upcoming absence, but then my boss said something really reassuring, along the lines that the cemetery was full of indispensable people, so he guessed they could spare me for this period. However, I was fortunate in that the company had a policy of paying full salary to anyone doing jury service.

I had been in my job with an offshore design consultancy for just over three years since finishing my MSc in ocean engineering at UCL. I really enjoyed the work, with a mixture of office design work, trips to construction sites, and the odd helicopter ride to oil or gas platforms out at sea. We were designing floating oil and gas platforms for water up to a 1,000 metres deep, and I was using to the full all I had learned from my studies in hydrodynamic wave analyses in the frequency domain. Sorry for the technical terms, but the point is that this includes a large amount of mathematical statistical and probabilistic analysis of random wave properties. Little did I know I would soon be applying these statistics in a completely different domain.

I also learned the limits of statistics. We had the 'hundred-year wave' that was the 'big one' which, as the name suggests, was only supposed to arrive once every one hundred years. The height of this wave was extrapolated from past statistics, so we designed our platforms to withstand it. Well, my boss told me a platform he had designed and installed some years back had no less than two different one-hundred-year waves hitting it in the first five years of its life. Spot the error! He invited me to read a book called *The Black Swan* by Nassim Taleb, which talks about how unlikely events are much more likely to happen than we realise.

This is because the real-life probability distributions of rare events do not follow the 'normal curve', but have fat tails at the extremes that increases their probabilities, which Taleb calls Black Swans (since everybody thought swans are white – until somebody discovered a black one). He wrote the book in 2006 and basically predicted the financial crisis two years later, since all the banks' risk models made the mistake of using the 'normal curve', which underestimated the risk of rare events. Apparently once the crisis was upon us, it turned out that the banks' models had said such a financial crisis could not happen in a billion years. Yet it did happen, and it seems crises like this regularly happen every ten years or so. I adored this book, and then promptly devoured Nassim Taleb's other three books on various misunderstandings of statistics.

Meanwhile, the oil price was also suffering from its own 'statistical anomaly', for which you should read that it was currently too low. A few people like me adore high oil prices since this means lots of work for new (and expensive) offshore oil and gas platforms. Our present project was an advanced study to test new concepts, but for the time being there were no oil companies queuing up to build one. Hence my boss' comment on me being eminently available for jury duty.

So, I arrived at the Central Criminal Court in EC4, commonly called the Old Bailey, at 9am on the Monday morning. The main building dated, I discovered, to 1902, and looked the typical Victorian / Edwardian monstrosity with neo-classic pillars, topped with a dome like a bell tower, and all built out of dirty grey limestone. I read the inscription above the main entrance, 'Defend the Children of the Poor & Punish the Wrongdoer'. It actually gave me a shiver down my spine; I suppose we all feel guilty about having done something we should not have. 'I was certainly not over the limit, your honour,' I imagined myself saying; 'the breathalyser was certainly malfunctioning.'

The Old Bailey now has no less than eighteen courtrooms inside, thanks to some more recent extensions. I showed my jury summons form to one of the receptionists, and she pointed me in the direction of one of the larger waiting rooms. Soon almost forty potential jurors gathered there, and we were told by one of the black-gowned ushers that there were two major murder trials just starting.

Murder trials? This could be interesting, I thought. Might one of them be the case of Sarah Richardson, charged with the double murder of her baby sons? It was splashed all over the newspapers. 'Multiple murderer mother finally to be brought to justice' said one headline on a tabloid, held in the hand of a potential juror not more than five feet from me. 'Cold killer hiding behind cot deaths?' asked another headline I had seen opposite me on the tube this morning. So, the press had already made up its mind.

We were each given a jury panel number, from 1 to 40. I was assigned jury panel number 6.

"If you are chosen, you will judge the facts," said the usher, "and the judge will judge the law. At ten o'clock we will split into two groups of twenty and go to the corresponding courtrooms for jury selection. If you are selected, you will return here every day for the two-to-four weeks we expect each trial to last. If you are not selected, you can return home. Meanwhile please leave anything you have brought with you, particularly mobile phones and laptops, in these lockers to your right. You may only take into the courtroom yourself, the locker key, handkerchiefs and any vital medicines you need during the day. Normally the judge allows you to take notes during the trial – we will provide the pens and notepaper. Do not at any time, at meal breaks, or in the evenings, attempt to do any research into the trial. Any jury member who sees or knows of another doing such research must immediately report it. Anybody doing such research must understand that they are committing an offense and will be immediately relieved of jury duty."

I looked at the other members of my group. There was a handful of people in their twenties like me, including a particularly striking girl. We were wearing a mixture of clothes from student jeans (a bit casual I thought), simple trousers or skirts with pullovers, to jackets and ties (like me). Then there was a collection of thirty- and forty-somethings. Some looked like agitated executives in their business suits or twinsets (they seemed particularly worried about losing their instantaneous contact to the office; what if an urgent email came up?); others looked more like bus drivers or receptionists wearing their best Friday night clothes (I say Friday, because nobody dresses up on Sundays any longer). There was also a collection of quite old people, in their fifties at least, some of whom might already be retired; they all had jackets and ties or reasonably smart dresses.

We were split into two groups, and at 10.15 twenty of us, numbers 1 to 20, were led into courtroom number 5. Sitting there already was the judge, the prosecution and defence teams, the court clerk, some ushers and already a good number of members of the public and press. There were twenty seats available in the jury box together with an overflow area just next to it.

It was an impressive moment. Here I was, a potential jury member, entering into the wood panelling of one of the fabled Old Bailey court rooms.

The court clerk, who was dressed like the barristers in wig and black gown, stood up. "We will now proceed with jury selection for the case of the Crown against Sarah Richardson," he said. Yes! It is indeed the double murder trial! I said to myself. This is going to be interesting.

The clerk told us that the case would be judged by the Honourable Mr Justice Braithwaite.

He then handed out to each of us a written notice that

'undertaking research into a case, communicating with another juror about this research and disclosing details of the deliberations of the jury are criminal offences for which the penalty is imprisonment or a fine, or both, and may be a contempt of court'.

Next he explained that he would read a list of names of witnesses that might be called during the trial. We must put our hand up if we personally knew or had any prior connection to any of these witnesses. The names were read out; I noticed there were several 'doctors' and 'professors'; nobody put their hand up.

After this I was expecting a long grilling for each jury member from the prosecution and defence, who would then use their vetoes strategically. But I've probably read too many John Grisham novels – and besides, this is not America. Apparently, counsel, who had our details, could only challenge a jury member under exceptional circumstances; neither the defence nor the prosecution issued any such challenges.

One by one the clerk randomly took jury numbers written on pieces of paper out of the little box in front of him. The first was number 16 – this was one of the forty something lady executives. She was told that she would be the jury foreperson, unless the jury wished to elect someone else. Several other jury members were then selected – numbers 3, 17, 11… We were well into the last third when I heard my number 6. At least I was in! In total, twelve jurors and two reserves were selected. The other six people were asked to leave. Well, I hoped this was going to be an interesting experience, after all it's not every day that you get to witness a real murder trial, let alone as a juror.

The court clerk spoke to the defendant. "Sarah Richardson, the names you are about to hear are the names of the jurors who will try you. If therefore you wish to object to them, or any of them, you must do so as they come to the book to be sworn, and before they are sworn, and your objection will be heard."

One by one the clerk came up to each juror. We had been told that we could adapt the oath to our specific faith or use a secular affirmation. When it came to my turn, I read out from the paper, "I swear by almighty God that I will faithfully try the defendant and give a true verdict according to the evidence." Most used the same oath. One person said, "I swear by Allah…", and two decided that they preferred the secular, "I solemnly, sincerely and truly declare and affirm…" Meanwhile the defendant did not object to anybody.

While the others were being sworn in, I mused about why I and others used the Christian oath rather than the secular affirmation. I am not exactly a practising churchgoer, but I had at least been christened. I decided it was because we all instinctively use 'Pascal's wager'. But surely Pascal invented the original concept of an 'option' well before the financial world did? You invest a small amount of effort (the price of the option) pretending to be religious, just in case God exists, all the time being pretty sure that he doesn't (the option is out of the money). When you eventually die you might find he does exist (the option is in the money), and so you go to heaven rather than to hell (a good payback); or you might find he doesn't exist (in which case you have only lost the modest price of the option). You see, engineers can read philosophy – although they might prefer the financial press; this is London, after all.

I was shaken out of my reveries when the very pretty girl I had spotted earlier sat down next to me after being sworn in. She was juror number 9, and I think the clerk had just called her Stephanie something.

The judge looked impressive in his scarlet robe with bits of fur sticking out, a black scarf and black band around his middle, a bit like those worn by people with backache. He also had a scarlet sash over his left shoulder, and he wore an old-fashioned white wing collar and white bands, which seemed to contrast with his rather yellowing wig, as if to illustrate the 'before and after' of being washed with Ariel washing powder.

"Ladies and gentlemen members of the jury, good morning," said the judge addressing us. "The evidence upon which you will decide the case is the evidence that will be presented to you here in court. As such, you should only discuss the case among yourselves and not with anyone else who may give a view but will not have heard the evidence. You should also not be influenced by any media reporting of the case and should not attempt to obtain further information about the case from anyone outside court, including using social media and the internet to contact witnesses or to otherwise conduct research.

"You have a collective responsibility as jurors to ensure you all act appropriately according to your oath or affirmation. As such, if you have any concerns during the trial, either relating to the improper conduct of another juror (for example, internet research) or to some other external factor (such as being approached by a third party regarding the case who attempts to influence you), you should immediately inform an usher who will notify me."

This was the third time in the same morning we were told that we were not allowed to do any research. Mobile phones, social media and Google searches must have really thrown a spanner in the works of court functioning for them to insist on this so much. Yet when you see all the conspiracy theories and fake news (the real fake news, not Trump's 'I don't like this news' version) that is floating around, you can understand that they prefer to avoid secondhand hearsay and to keep to the facts, or at least to people's version of the facts under oath.

The judge continued. "Matters of law are for me alone, as judge, to consider; so, if any legal applications are made during the trial, I will ask the jury to leave court while they are dealt with. Do not try to speak with or contact anyone in the courtroom. If you are unsure about anything, and if you think it's important, I ask you to write it down in a concise manner, then catch the eye of the court clerk here, Mr Jonathan Granger, who will pass the message to me." The clerk nodded to us. "Finally, we estimate that this trial could last approximately two weeks, but it might take longer. The court will sit every weekday from 10am to 1pm, and then from 2pm to 4.30pm.

"My name is Justice Braithwaite. Since this is the Old Bailey, there is a tradition here that counsel calls all judges 'My Lord'; but I can assure you I am a common mortal and I am certainly not a Lord. At least not yet." There was a ripple of laughter around the courtroom. So, the judge seemed human; but he probably always said that. "I will introduce the counsel for the Crown, Mr Peter Scott, QC, assisted by Mr Timothy Sturdee; and the counsel for the

defence, Mr Eugene Dawkins, assisted by Mr Gordon Hill."
Each of the barristers turned and nodded towards us in turn
in their rather ridiculous wigs. Ah, so the prosecution could
afford a 'silk' – a Queen's Counsellor – a very senior rank of
barrister, but not the defendant. Was that fair?

"Now that these preliminaries have been dealt with,"
continued the judge, "we will break for lunch, and afterwards
the prosecution will open its case."

We all stood up as he left the courtroom.

Chapter Two

Two of the ushers had meanwhile morphed into being the jury keepers, basically our babysitters. They led us out to the jury room where an outside caterer had laid out our lunch on a side table. 'Lunch' was not the right word. They were sandwiches followed by fruit yoghurt.

I sat down with a plateful next to Stephanie. "I hate sandwiches," I said to break the ice. "They make you fat by combining the carbohydrates with the saturated fats; at least that's what the French expert Michel Montignac says in his book *Eat Yourself Slim*. Have you read it?"

"No," she replied. "But I think there's is some truth in that."

"Montignac became a millionaire selling his books, basically because he allows you to gorge on greasy steaks, as long as you eat it with a salad and not with chips. But I think his millions really came from him saying you can drink half a litre of wine a day without putting on weight; that's certainly what attracted me to his books."

"Well, I don't think you need to worry about your weight, you look pretty healthy." She said. This is a good start, I thought. "So, you can eat your sandwiches like a grown man!" Ouch. "Did your Mr Montignac follow his own advice?"

"I assume he did. He lived all the way to the great age of sixty-six." That got a smile out of her. "Anyway, I'm sure French juries have a lunch of boeuf bourguignon with haricots verts, washed down with a good Côte de Beaune…"

"And then sleep all through the afternoon court session."

"What do you do when you're not judging murderers?" I asked her.

"I'm a nurse in intensive care in Saint Bartholomew's, well, a sister, actually."

"I'm impressed. You must have moved fast to become a sister at your age."

"Well, I do have to be quick; most of our intensive care patients are men. And most have had heart surgery, because they ate too many saturated fats. So apart from eating steaks, what do you do?" she asked me.

"I'm an engineer who designs offshore oil platforms." Normally a good line with the girls.

Her eyes sort of glazed over. "Well, somebody has to do it, I suppose," she said.

By one o'clock everyone had been to the loo and we were back in our jury box.

All the court players were sitting in their places, ready to play their parts and look important. The judge, the court clerk, the barristers all in their wigs, winged collars, bands and robes; the ushers also in their robes. It reminded me a bit of my undergraduate days in Cambridge where we had to wear our gowns for candle-lit formal hall, even if we only had jeans and sweatshirts on underneath. (It certainly helped keep your clothes clean when the serving staff spilt the soup down your back, which happened rather often.)

The defence solicitor was sitting behind the defence barristers – no robe or anything, very much a second-class citizen; and I assume it was his opposite number, also in civvies, from the Crown Prosecution Service sitting behind his barristers. In the American films the lawyers do everything, the paperwork and the court drama. Here it is split up between the solicitor, who is paid by the client, who then must find, brief and pay a barrister and his junior. That nicely triples the size of the defence team and the legal fees. I wondered if important information got lost with this rather cumbersome chain of instruction.

Mr Peter Scott, QC, stood up. His robes looked impressive, but then they were made out of black silk.

"Ladies and gentlemen of the jury. The defendant, Sarah Richardson, is accused of murder. She is only formally charged with one count of murder of her second son, George Richardson, who died on the 14th of April of this year at the age of four weeks. However, there is evidence to suggest she also killed her first son, Andrew Richardson, in June 2017, when he was six weeks old."

"The case is quite simple," he continued, and at the same time hooked his thumbs behind the lapels of his robe. I could not believe he was really doing that; too classic, the gesture must have been burnt into him as a boy watching his schoolmasters. I supposed he was trying to impress us.

21

"One unexplained infant death due to natural causes can happen. It is called S.I.D.S., sudden infant death syndrome, more commonly known as cot death. Our expert witness – a leading paediatrics professor – will testify that there is a small possibility for this to happen. Once. He will also show you that the chance, the probability, of it happening a second time is so small that it is impossible to happen by accident.

"Furthermore, the post-mortem examination shows signs around the mouth consistent with smothering. Then, there is the suspicious behaviour of the defendant who, once the incident has happened, first calls her husband but not an ambulance.

"As to why, we will learn that Mrs Richardson is diagnosed with a pathology called F.D.I.A. – factitious disorder imposed on another. This is where a mother creates the appearance of health problems in her child in order to gain sympathy. Serious sufferers of this disorder are known to have gone so far as to kill their children.

"By Mrs Richardson's own admissions, she hadn't wanted children so fast, because they interfered with her career. Furthermore, she was exhausted beyond breaking point by looking after them. These are two very clear motives to go from inventing health problems to the full act of committing murder."

I saw the defendant look up sharply while these comments were being made and she shook her head. Either she was pained to hear them, I thought, or she was genuinely concerned that her words had been twisted out of context; or maybe she was just putting on a good act.

At this juncture the lead defence council also shook his

head in dismay and tried standing up to object. But he was put down by the Judge, who said, "Mr Dawkins, please do not interrupt the prosecution's summary. First, you can give any counter-arguments in a few minutes when you give your defence summary. More importantly the jury will hear the evidence from witnesses that either corroborates or not these statements." He nodded to the prosecution to continue.

Scott carried on with his summary. "We are only formally charging for the murder of her second child, George. However, the conditions in which both children died were remarkably similar: they were of a similar age, each death happened around 8pm, each time the husband was absent and she was on her own without any nanny or au pair present, each time suspicious symptoms were discovered by the pathologist."

"That is the case the Crown will present to you in the coming days," said Scott, winding up. "Here is a copy of the indictment that accuses Mrs Sarah Richardson of one count of murder of her son George Richardson." Scott handed copies to one of the ushers, who then handed it out to all of us in the jury.

Eugene Dawkins, the barrister for the defence, got to his feet. He did not have the frock coat and waistcoat of the prosecuting barrister, just a dark grey suit. And the gown he wore over it was obviously just cloth and not silk. But then, I thought to myself, he's not a QC, is he? But he did have the same winged collar with bands, and the horsehair wig, that looked like it had 1950s curlers in it. He did not hook his thumbs behind his robe lapels.

"Ladies and gentlemen. The defence will demonstrate

to you that in no way is Mrs Richardson a killer. She is a loving mother whom tragedy has struck twice in a row; she has lost both her sons to a well-known but little understood syndrome called S.I.D.S., cot death.

"For George Richardson's death, the coroner was formal – *death by natural causes*, based on the pathologist's report. Yes, the pathologist's report also mentions certain marks around the baby's mouth. The prosecution maintains, erroneously, that this was deliberate smothering. We will show that this is due quite simply to the mother's valiant attempt at artificial resuscitation. For twenty minutes. To no avail. She now knew the baby was dead, so she phoned her husband to share the tragic news. That is not suspicious, that is just normal.

"The prosecution offers diverse and totally invented motives, and then they say it was Mrs Richardson's own statements that confirm them. These statements are quoted out of all context, tiny bits of a conversation plucked from several hours of interviews with the police, in the total absence of any lawyer. Mrs Richardson willingly answered all their questions, not believing that this nightmare of an accusation could possibly be for real. We will provide all the witnesses necessary to prove those accusations false.

"Finally, the prosecution will bring out an 'expert' to 'prove' that a double cot death is a very rare event." For this last phrase you could hear his voice dripping with well-rehearsed disdain and scepticism. "But since when are you guilty of murder simply because you have had a double dose of bad luck? On the contrary, if a cot death can strike once, then there is every risk that it can strike again.

"Many people never accepted that it was an accidental

24

death for Diana Princess of Wales. Why? Because, such a beautiful and much-loved princess cannot die in a banal car accident; it has to be assassination! In my cross-examinations I will show you this is what has happened here, how a fantasy murder has replaced the banal reality of tragedy. If you are struck by lightning it is bad luck; who says you can't be struck by lightning twice? As unlikely as it seems, it has happened, several times. I will show you how it's just *very* bad luck. Others, in this courtroom, will suggest that it's so unlikely it has to be deliberate. We are warned not to fall into the trap of fake news and conspiracy theories. I ask you, the jury, to do the same here in this courtroom. Thank you." The defence sat down.

"Thank you, Mr Dawkins," said the judge. "However, such *qualitative* ideas would have been much better placed in your closing remarks. I asked simply for your opening statement on how you outline your defence. But let's move on. Mr Scott, please call the first witness for the prosecution."

Chapter Three

A youngish man in spectacles and a prematurely receding hairline was ushered into court and shown the witness stand. The usher gave him a piece of paper and asked him to read it out. "I swear by almighty God that the evidence I shall give shall be the truth, the whole truth and nothing but the truth."

Mr Peter Scott, QC, stood up for the prosecution. "Please state your name and profession."

"I am Dr Rodney Harris. I am a pathologist at Lambeth Hospital."

"Did you do the autopsy on George Richardson, baby son of Daniel and Sarah Richardson, who died on the 14th of April of this year?"

"Yes, I did."

"Did you find any signs of illness or any other internal disorders?"

"No, I did not."

"Could you ascertain the cause of death?"

"No, not really."

"Did you find any indications that could lead you to think that this might be a suspicious death?"

"Yes. There were marks around the mouth where the skin colouring was different."

"Bruising?"

"Yes, sort of."

"What is bruising, Dr Harris?"

"It's when blood capillaries are broken by external pressure, so blood seeps out into the adjacent skin tissue."

"Is it possible to cause bruising in a body after death?"

"No. If blood is not being pumped by the heart, it cannot escape from the blood vessels."

"So, bruising can only happen to a body that is still alive?"

"Yes."

"Then you could not create bruising by trying to resuscitate a dead baby's body?"

"No."

"Could such bruises have been caused by a pillow or other object being used to suffocate the baby?"

The defence stood up. "My Lord, my learned friend is leading the witness."

"I agree," said the judge. "Mr Scott, please rephrase your question."

"Could such bruises have been caused by a pillow or other object being applied under pressure to the baby's mouth?" asked Scott.

"Yes," replied Harris.

"Is this why you signal in your report, on page 12, the possibility of a suspicious death?"

"Yes, it is."

"Thank you. That's all from me." Scott sat down.

The lead defence barrister got to his feet for the cross examination. "Dr Harris, how many autopsies have you performed on babies in your career?" asked Dawkins.

"Two or three."

"Two, or three, which is it?"

"Three with George Richardson," replied Harris.

"How many were considered as cases of S.I.D.S., or cot deaths?"

"Not for the first two. They were both clear cases of illness with infection as cause of death. For George Richardson, it is considered as one of the possible causes."

"So, you confirm that the death may be due to S.I.D.S.?"

"Yes. But I also flagged the possibility of other causes such as suffocation."

"From what you have just told us, you have never done an autopsy on any other baby that had died of suffocation?"

"No."

"Have you done an autopsy on any person that has died of suffocation?"

"No."

"How old are you Dr Harris?"

"Twenty-seven."

"How many autopsies have you done in total as a qualified pathologist?"

"Fifteen."

"Fifteen?"

"Yes, I only qualified last year."

"In all transparency, how many autopsies does a pathologist have to do before he is considered an expert?"

"More than a hundred, I suppose."

"We all have to begin somewhere, there's nothing wrong with that," said Dawkins kindly. "By your own admission you are nowhere near being an expert yet. Did you ask another more experienced pathologist for a second opinion?"

"No," replied Harris.

"Why not?"

"We have very few resources. We can't have two pathologists doing every autopsy."

"But here we are talking about possible murder; and yet you, an inexperienced pathologist, did not look for a second opinion? I ask again, why not?" Now Dawkins was a little less kindly.

"I repeat, lack of resources," insisted Harris.

"May I suggest another reason?" countered Dawkins. "You considered this to be a simple cot death, and only mentioned the marks around the mouth to cover your backside?"

Peter Scott, QC, was on his feet. "My Lord, the question asked by my learned friend goes to the witness' character, which is impermissible."

"Mr Dawkins," said the judge. "Nice try, but please keep within the rules. Please rephrase your question."

I was amazed at the courtesy of all parties. Maybe I had seen too many American court dramas, where the attorneys leap to their feet with 'Objection, your honour', and the judge would growl 'sustained' or 'overruled'! Well, I thought, this is what makes us British, with our politeness and everything. Or is it just the wigs that make them play a role like in some old-fashioned film? "My learned friend… it goes to the witness' character…" And the judge replies, just as politely, "Nice try, but please keep within the rules…" I went to some minor public school, but I didn't learn this etiquette. So, I suppose the accent should be on the 'minor' and not on the 'public' (as in 'private' – go work that one out!). Stop your mind wandering, I scolded myself, and concentrate on what the lawyers, sorry barristers, are saying!

Suitably admonished, but doubtless happy to have got his point over to the jury, Dawkins tried again. "Dr Harris. Did you *not* look for a second opinion because in your mind, and despite the presence of those marks, you really *did* consider this to be a natural death?"

"Yes, I suppose so."

"In your fourteen other autopsies, did you ever conclude that there was a suspicious death?"

"No, not yet."

"Then am I right to conclude that you do not yet have much forensic experience in analysing suspicious marks?"

Scott was on his feet again. "My Lord, this is conjecture."

"Let him answer the question," said the judge.

"I suppose not," replied Harris.

"Are you sure you can tell the difference between a mark caused by bruising before death, with a mark caused by blood draining to other parts of the body in different patterns after death?" continued Dawkins.

"I'm not sure I follow you."

"If the mother applied pressure with her lips onto a small body that had already died, and probably in her anxiety her lips were wrapped firmly around her teeth and gums, is it not possible that this pressure might cause the blood to drain differently from those areas concerned, leaving marks visible during the autopsy?"

"Yes. I imagine it is possible."

"So those marks could be created by the mother's resuscitation attempts after the baby is dead?"

"Yes, possibly," conceded the pathologist.

"No further questions, my Lord." Dawkins sat down.

"Do you wish to re-examine, Mr Scott?" asked the judge.

There was a rapid whispered discussion between the lead and junior prosecution counsel. Then Scott got to his feet. "Just one question, my Lord. Dr Harris, the mother claims in her police statement to have tried, alternatively with her mouth-to-mouth resuscitation, to have provided cardiac massage by pumping down on the rib cage with her hands. Did you see similar marks on the ribcage as to those you found around the mouth?"

"No, not that I remember."

"Thank you. That is all," said Scott, sitting down.

"If there are no further questions, you may leave, Dr Harris," said the judge. "Please call the next witness for the prosecution."

Chapter Four

He was in his late forties, in a rather shiny dark suit that looked to have come off the peg in Marks & Spencer, but some time ago. When he was sworn in, he spoke with an authoritative, but unmistakably 'estuary', voice. It was obvious he had done this many times before. The prosecution asked him to state his name and profession, but the whole court had already guessed what he did for a living.

After these preliminaries, Scott got straight to the point. "Detective Sergeant Tooley, how did you get involved in this investigation?"

"I got a phone call from someone in the local coroner's office. He said I should look into two consecutive cases of infant deaths within the same family – the Richardsons."

"Why was this person suspicious?"

"Two reasons," he explained. "The first was, of course, the pathologist's report that noted the possibility of a suspicious death due to the marks around the mouth of baby George, the second child to die. This led him to do some research into double cot deaths, where he found his second reason, the 'cot-death law' – 'one cot death is a tragedy, two deaths are a crime, unless proved otherwise'. He said I should contact Professor Goodwin of the University of East Anglia, who was an expert in this field."

"So, what did you do then?" asked Scott.

"I dug out the original details for the death of the first child, Andrew," answered Tooley. "The autopsy report concluded no known cause of death, so it was put down as S.I.D.S., cot death, which led the coroner to conclude an accidental death. However, the autopsy also mentioned some retinal haemorrhages that could have been created by the baby being violently shaken. This got me even more suspicious.

"Then, since my contact had mentioned Professor Goodwin, I looked him up on the internet," Tooley continued. "He's a professor of paediatrics at the University of East Anglia. I saw that he was indeed one of the clear experts in the domain of infant deaths. I contacted him, briefed him on the situation, and he expressed a marked interest in the case.

"He told me that the probability of two sequential cot deaths in the same family was next to zero; we went through the arithmetic together, and it became clear to me that this could only mean foul play. What's more, the pathologist's reports of a shaken baby for the first child, followed by a suggestion of smothering for the second, were both clinchers. Professor Goodwin was quite clear; I should go and investigate who had been present at the time of the baby's death and arrest them for murder.

"The pathologist's report showed 8pm as the probable

time of death. The statements from the inquest gave 7pm as the time of the mother's arrival home, and the au pair left to go out shortly after that. I checked Mr Richardson's alibi; he was indeed with other persons at that time in the Bistro Mirey restaurant in West Kensington." (He pronounced it 'By-strow'.) "Furthermore, the accused's statements confirm all of this."

"So," said Scott, "the only person in the Richardson's flat at the time of death was Sarah Richardson?"

"Yes."

"Did you discover any other important elements in your investigation?"

"Yes," continued Tooley. "I found the sequence of calls made by Mrs Richardson to be very suspicious. Both according to her phone records and according to her own statement, she called her husband before calling for an ambulance.

"In her statement, she clearly says she tried to resuscitate the baby. If that was the case, she would also have called for an ambulance. She could have called 999 with one hand, while doing cardiac massage with the other, put it on loudspeaker, and continue with her efforts while calling. No, nothing like that. She just calls her husband to say the baby's dead. And only then, once he has asked whether she has called an ambulance, does she ring off and call for one.

"So, once I had got all my evidence tied up, I discussed with my superior officers, and got the warrant to arrest Mrs Richardson for murder."

"I understand you then interviewed Mrs Richardson at some length?" asked Scott.

"Yes, I did," said Tooley.

"And did she tell you anything more of interest?"

Looking at these two experienced players – the prosecution barrister and the police detective – batting backwards and forwards, it was obvious that they had rehearsed together.

"Yes," said Tooley. "She clearly indicated that she didn't want those children, or at least not so soon, because they were a severe handicap on her career."

"Anything else?"

"Yes, she complained how both her babies had kept her awake at night, by crying consistently, refusing to feed, vomiting, and so on. She said it made her incredibly tired and irritated. She said that at times she was at the end of her tether."

"Thank you, DS Tooley. That's very clear. I have no further questions." Scott sat down.

Later I gleaned what was going through Sarah Richardson's mind at this time:

'They are totally twisting my words out of context. Yes, those boys came earlier than expected, particularly the second one - we never expected I would get pregnant again so fast. Yes, we had to reorganise my job around them. But between nannies and au pair girls, I was never off for more than a few weeks. My company fully accepted this! I loved those baby boys! They fully became my life. I did and would have done anything for them. I would sacrifice anything to get them back. I told the police all that. When I talked to them, I imagined that it was all a big mistake, that by telling them everything about us they would soon realise that.

'Of course, I got tired and irritable, what mother doesn't with a new-born baby? I told them that. But I also told them

I have never loved another being so much; those babies came from me; they were part of me! Why do they invent this story where I am the villain?

'To imagine that I could hurt my babies! What inhumanity makes them think that? Even when I told them everything about me, answered every one of their questions, they twist it around to make it sound the opposite of what I said, or the opposite of anything I could possibly do to hurt my loved ones.

'Why are they so warped? Why did I lose not one but both of my loved babies – what mother could suffer that? Then they add insult to injury by saying I murdered them. This is a nightmare without end. When will it end?

'I do have full faith in the English justice system. This court will see that I could never have done what they are accusing me of. Won't it?'

Now the lead defence stood up and glanced at his notes. "Detective Sergeant Tooley," said Dawkins, "please read us the conclusion of the coroner's report at the inquest. I'll give you a copy to refresh your memory. Here it is on page 11."

Tooley took the report passed to him and started reading the highlighted passage. "Cause of death unknown. Most probably sudden infant death syndrome, S.I.D.S., more commonly known as cot death."

"Can you confirm that the coroner's conclusion does not suggest any suspicious circumstances concerning this death?" asked Dawkins.

"No, but the pathologist's report had questions about the marks around the mouth," answered Tooley.

"The same pathologist's report that was used for the

coroner to come to his conclusions," Dawkins pointed out. "But I was talking about the coroner's report. Is there any mention of suspicious death?"

"No," the detective admitted.

"Was it the coroner himself who later contacted you to open an investigation?"

"No, it was someone in the coroner's office."

"Who?" insisted Dawkins.

"I prefer not to say," Tooley said somewhat uneasily. "Our discussion was purely off the record. He suggested I should contact Professor Goodwin and come to my own conclusions."

"Ah, the famous Professor Goodwin, whom we shall be meeting later as the prosecution's expert witness," Dawkins shot back with a certain scepticism. "Please go to page 6 of the coroner's report and read the highlighted section."

Tooley read out as asked. "The death certificate signed by Dr Harris of Lambeth's Hospital cites the death 'most probably as S.I.D.S., especially in view of the fact that the family has already suffered a S.I.D.S. death'."

"So, this confirms that the coroner was fully aware about the first cot death before coming to his conclusion for the second death?"

"Obviously, yes," replied Tooley.

"But someone else in his office," commented Dawkins with a certain disdain in his voice, "someone you are not prepared to name, preferred the conspiracy theory that this was double murder, and then put you onto this wild goose chase?"

"My Lord," said the prosecution as he was rising to his feet. "I feel that my learned friend is straying from the facts into the land of conjecture, which is detrimental to the understanding of this case."

"Well," replied the judge, "as you well know, council does have a lot more leeway when they are *cross*-examining, and so in this case leading questions can be tolerated. However, Mr Dawkins, please could you ask a more specific question?"

"Detective Sergeant Tooley," said Dawkins clearly, "what *new* information did your contact in the coroner's office have, that was not available and known by the coroner himself, that caused him to have a different opinion?"

"I suppose that it was his learning of the existence of the 'cot death law'."

"I see," continued the defence in a tone that suggested he certainly did not see; then he changed the subject. "Concerning the order of the phone calls. You said all she had to do was to call an ambulance even while doing her resuscitation. Where do ladies normally keep their telephones?"

"In their handbags, I guess," replied the policeman.

"And when in their own home, going from room to room, does a lady normally carry her handbag with her, or does she leave it somewhere, like on the hall table?"

"I take your point," conceded Tooley.

"Are you aware that when Sarah Richardson was in her school sixth form, she obtained the Gold Duke of Edinburgh Award?" asked Dawkins.

"No, I'm not aware of that."

"So perhaps you are not aware that as part of her D. of E. community service activities, she chose to attend training in advanced first aid?"

"No."

"Would it surprise you to know that advanced first aid covers C.P.R., that is cardiopulmonary resuscitation. This involves mouth-to-mouth breathing, cardiac massage and the various techniques to detect a heartbeat pulse on the wrist or under the chin?"

"No, that doesn't surprise me. As police officers we undergo similar training."

"Is it not then legitimate that, after such medical training and experience, Mrs Richardson should be able to determine with a high degree of accuracy whether another person is dead or still alive?" insisted Dawkins.

"I guess so," Tooley admitted. "But even then, you never know. You always ring for an ambulance just in case."

"Have you ever lost a child, Detective Sergeant?"

"No."

"Mrs Richardson had. She lost her first baby. She knew what a dead baby looked like; she had already experienced this. Indeed, in one of her own statements, did she not say that she was almost certain he was dead before she tried to resuscitate him?"

"Yes, she did."

"So, is it not legitimate," insisted Dawkins, "that if you know your baby is already dead, and you have spent twenty minutes trying to resuscitate him without success, that you might call the baby's father first? He is the father, her husband; he needs to know and share this tragic news. And what good will an ambulance do now? Can you not admit that?"

"Yes," acquiesced Tooley half-heartedly.

"So, if Professor Goodwin had not told you his famous

statistical analysis of the likelihood of two deaths, would you have pursued this investigation further?"

"No," admitted Tooley. "But his explanation was crystal clear," he added somewhat on the defensive.

"Finally, once you had arrested Mrs Richardson, you talked with her for some time, didn't you?"

"Yes."

"How long exactly, please?" asked Dawkins. "I have the transcript here if necessary, to jog your memory."

"About four hours."

"Did she have a lawyer present?"

"No."

"No? You had just arrested her for murder, and she was freely talking to you without a lawyer? For four hours?"

"Yes," replied the policeman.

"Is that the usual behaviour of somebody who has something to hide?"

"It could be a very good tactic to pretend to be innocent."

"In those four hours, did she tell you if she loved her babies?"

"Er, yes, she did say that."

"Did she say she could not have harmed them?"

"Yes, that as well."

"Did she explain how for each birth she was able to organise her job with her firm, and then come back to work quite soon afterwards through a system of nannies or au pair girls?"

"Yes," said Tooley.

"Did she explain to you that her firm has excellent role models of women who are fully advancing in their careers after a number of children thanks to their top rate equal opportunities policies?"

"Yes, she did."

"Did she tell you how in her discussions with other young mothers, she found that they were all equally as tired as her? And that gave her the courage to carry on because she felt less alone?"

"Yes."

"And when the prosecution asked you for important elements from this discussion, you chose not to mention all that?" Dawkins asked with indignation. "You just summarised four hours of discussions into two short statements, plucked out of all context, that fitted in with your unlikely hypothesis?"

"No, not at all," replied Tooley. "I consider those comments about the impact of her pregnancies on her career, and her acute tiredness, to be key parts of her statement."

"Detective Sergeant, you weren't trying to corroborate her story. You had decided she had to be guilty due to some questionable statistics from some so-called expert, and you were uniquely fishing for bits of information that went along with your preconceived ideas. Admit it."

"No, I was doing standard police work. The case against her was strong. Anything she said was important to that case."

"No further questions." The defence sat down.

"Re-examination, Mr Scott?" the judge asked the prosecution.

Scott glanced at his junior Sturdee, who shook his head. "No, my Lord," said Scott.

"Detective Sergeant Tooley, you may go," said the judge.

Chapter Five

"Mr Scott, please call your next witness," asked the judge.

"The Crown calls Professor Michael Goodwin."

The judge turned to the jury. "Members of the jury, most witnesses are not allowed to listen to the proceedings in the court. They wait outside before giving their testimony. Normally there is one exception, that of an expert witness. He can listen to all the testimonies so as to have a global view of the proceedings. However, when I learned that our expert witness, Professor Goodwin, had been involved in the case even before the arrest was made, I decided that he must be treated like any other witness. So, he has not been present in court up until now."

Professor Goodwin entered the courtroom and walked up to the witness stand. He was well into his sixties. He was impeccably dressed in a dark suit, white shirt and what looked like a Trinity College Cambridge tie. My first degree at Cambridge had taught me something about ties. That, and how to down a pint of beer very fast – something that had been much more useful to me in the after-hour pubs near our oil platform construction sites then had my engineering degree, at least as viewed by burly Scottish welders. Something told me Professor Goodwin did not spend much time downing pints in such pubs.

He also took the oath without reading the words offered by the usher. He had done this before. The real expert witness. However, when he spoke, I was somewhat reassured; he definitely had a bit of a Norfolk accent underneath all his outside polish.

Peter Scott, QC, started the ball rolling. "Professor Goodwin, since you are here today as an expert witness, please could you tell us your experience and credentials."

"Good afternoon. My name is Michael Goodwin. I was born in Norwich and studied medicine at Trinity College, Cambridge. I qualified as a doctor in 1980 at Addenbrooke's Hospital in Cambridge, some thirty-nine years ago now. My speciality, which started then and has continued since, has always been paediatrics. I have had a career combining practicing clinical medicine, together with university teaching and research. I was appointed professor of paediatrics at the University of East Anglia in 2003, while continuing my clinical practice at the associated Norfolk and Norwich teaching hospital. My particular area of expertise is in child abuse, where in all humility I am regarded as the country's leading expert, and we could extend that to say that I am one of the world's leading experts."

"And were you not knighted in 2009 for services to child health, Sir Michael?"

"Yes, I was. But please, I do prefer the simple title of Professor."

How modest of him, I thought.

"How many publications do you have, Professor Goodwin?" continued Scott.

"In total 225. But of course, these include publications on research led by my researchers under my direction."

"Do you consider yourself to be an expert into infant deaths?"

"Yes, twenty-eight of my publications are dedicated to this subject."

"Please then give us your expert analysis of the death of George Richardson on the 14th of April of this year."

"I was able to obtain all of Mrs Richardson's NHS case files," explained Goodwin. "She was diagnosed with post-natal depression even before the death of her first son Andrew. Following his death, she has been considered to be in a more or less permanent general depression, which continued after the death of her second son, and continues to this day. Now, from these case files and discussions I had with the prison doctor, I diagnose that Mrs Richardson is also suffering from factitious disorder imposed on another – F.D.I.A. for short." Goodwin seemed in his element. "This condition is strongly linked to her ongoing depressions. This is where a caregiver creates the appearance of health problems in another person, typically their child. The primary motive is to gain attention, and is often caused by abuse to that person when they themselves were a child. It is quite typical of a mother suffering from F.D.I.A. to deliberately try to smother her child, we even have surveillance videos of different mothers attempting this in various hospitals. Often it only arises in injury for the child, so that the parent can get sympathy from medical professionals. But sometimes it results in death."

"You confirm that parents suffering from F.D.I.A. have been known to kill their own children?" asked the prosecution.

"Yes, I do confirm that," answered Goodwin. "We have several clearly proven cases of this."

"What other factors led you to conclude that the death of George Richardson was deliberate?"

"The two pathologists' reports were clear. For the first death, that of Andrew, the retinal haemorrhages are certain signs of a shaken baby. For the second death, George, the bruising around the mouth signifies smothering. Both symptoms converging with my diagnosis of F.D.I.A."

"Any other factors, Professor?" asked Scott.

Just like with the police officer, it was clear these two had practiced their batting sequence.

"Ah!" The Professor nodded. This was the question he had obviously been waiting for. "The chances of two consecutive cases of S.I.D.S. (sudden infant death syndrome, or cot deaths) are so infinitesimally small, that it is effectively impossible. The probability is one in 72 million against. There's more chance that an outsider horse, with eighty-to-one odds against, would win four grand nationals in a row!" Goodwin smiled at his own explanation.

"Please could you explain how you calculate this probability," asked Scott.

"It's very simple," Goodwin answered in his best lecture room voice. "For an affluent non-smoking family, the probability of S.I.D.S. is one infant dying for 8,500 healthy births. *One* death. But the probability of two deaths is the square of this figure: one in 8,500 times one in 8,500, that gives us one in 72 million. This analysis is the origin of the cot death law: one death is a tragedy; two deaths is a crime."

I could not believe my ears. Was this guy serious? Even basic GCSE maths taught you to have more respect for probability. What about sample size? What about testing the null hypothesis? What about statistical dependence? And he was a professor!

"So, Professor Goodwin," the prosecution continued, "please confirm to the court exactly what is your expert opinion on these deaths."

Goodwin spoke slowly and clearly for maximum effect. "The chances of two natural deaths in a row are so low at one in 72 million that certainly the second death, and probably both deaths, have to be murder."

I could not restrain myself. "Bullshit! He's massacring statistics!" I shouted out loud. All heads in the courtroom seemed to jerk round in my direction. My neighbour Stephanie looked at me in an alarmed fashion.

"Juror number 6!" cried the judge. "You will *not* utter any comments during court! You will keep any and all opinions to yourself until the time has come for jury deliberation. Then, and only then, will you be free to express them. It is the defence's role to challenge this witness, not yours. Do you understand?"

"Yes, sir!" I replied meekly, avoiding any eye contact.

"Please continue, Mr Scott."

The prosecution seemed quite worried by my outburst; but then, a hostile jury member is naturally off-putting if you are looking for a conviction. Very quickly Scott steered the testimony back on course. "Professor, you said that the chances of two natural deaths in a row are so low at one in 72 million that it has to be murder. And you attribute this to the mother suffering from a disorder called F.D.I.A.?"

"Yes, that is correct," Goodwin said sternly and a little too loudly. He was obviously not used to having his authority challenged by someone the age of his medical students.

"Could you confirm your opinions as to how these intentional deaths happened?" continued Scott.

"I repeat what I have already said," answered Goodwin. "As per the autopsy report on Andrew Richardson in 2017, his death was due to excessive shaking. And the cause of the second death of infant George Richardson earlier this year is clearly marked in the autopsy report. The signs around the mouth indicate smothering. Both these events are entirely consistent with F.D.I.A."

"Thank you, Professor. No further questions at this stage."

As the prosecution sat down, defence barrister Eugene Dawkins stood up.

Right, I thought to myself. It's at last time for someone to knock holes in this professor's methodology.

"Professor Goodwin, I understand you testify quite often in these types of trials?"

"Yes, I am seen to be an expert in this domain."

"How much do you get for testifying? What is your fee?"

"I'm not sure that this question is relevant. Of course I have a fee, my time is valuable; today while in court I am not able to see patients; coming up to London creates travel and hotel costs."

"Is not your fee five thousand pounds, each time, Professor?"

"Er, yes, about that."

"Before you took on this case," said Dawkins, "did you not receive a false report that the defendant had made a call to a criminal lawyer at the time of her child's death, before calling for the ambulance?"

The prosecution was on his feet. "My Lord, we all agreed previously that there are no grounds for this rumour. Checks on phone records show this is absolutely not the case. I really don't know why the defence insists on raking it up."

"My point, "said Dawkins, "is not whether the rumour is true – it is not. My point is whether Professor Goodwin investigated this case already biased by a report which was falsely prejudicial to the defendant."

"I accept the question," said the judge. "Professor Goodwin, please answer."

"Yes, the police did mention that such a rumour existed," said Goodwin uneasily, "and that they were in the process of checking it out."

"In the light of this rumour, did that not make you consider that the defendant was already guilty, even before considering the other evidence?" asked Dawkins.

"No, absolutely not," said Goodwin unconvincingly. "My opinion was, and is, entirely based on the medical evidence and on the impossibly small probability of double cot deaths."

"Professor Goodwin," said Dawkins. "You are aware, I believe, that we have consulted with Professor Roger Hudson, who is, as you well know, an eminent eye surgeon. He has examined the pathologist's slides prepared in 2017 for the post-mortem of Andrew Richardson, the first son, and formally states there is no sign of retinal haemorrhages. He will be testifying later in this trial that the pathologist was mistaken, and that he mistook some shadows for haemorrhages."

"Yes, I am aware," said Goodwin, "and have already written a report countering my colleague's claim."

"Are you an expert on eyes, Professor?"

"No, but I know more about abuse and shaken babies than my esteemed colleague."

"Was there any other evidence in the pathologist's report pointing to a shaken baby syndrome, other than in the retinal slides?"

"No, not directly. But I stand by *my* professional opinion."

"Professor, this time you may not be aware of the result of my cross-examination this morning of Dr Rodney Harris of Lambeth Hospital, the pathologist who did the post-mortem on the second child, George Richardson. He never was sure what caused the marks around the mouth. He formally admitted that, rather than being bruising before death, it may have another very simple and innocent explanation: that it is due to the blood draining differently from the tissues after the baby's death, due to the pressure applied during the mother's attempts at artificial resuscitation."

"No, I am not aware of this newly invented hypothesis, which based on the evidence I have seen, I reject. Dr Harris is mistaken. My diagnosis remains the same, it was death by suffocation."

"Did you personally examine the dead child?"

"No, I did not."

"Are you a pathologist, Professor?"

"No, but…"

"Then how can your diagnosis trump that of a qualified pathologist who did the post-mortem?" interrupted Dawkins angrily.

"Once again, I know more about child abuse than any pathologist. That child was suffocated," Goodwin retorted adamantly.

"Professor Goodwin," said Dawkins, "this so-called cot death law, one death is a tragedy, another death is a crime until proved otherwise… is it not also called 'Goodwin's law'?"

"Yes, it is."

"Named after yourself?" asked Dawkins. "Were you at the origin of this law?"

"Yes, I was," replied Goodwin a little proudly.

"Do other practitioners use it? Have there been court cases where other experts have used it?"

"Yes, a few other experts use it. But most often it is me who is called as the medical profession's best expert."

"And who," asked Dawkins, "was the doctor who discovered F.D.I.A. – factitious disorder imposed on another?"

"Again, that would be me," Goodwin answered, with the same hint of pride.

"Based on what analysis?"

"I analysed eighty-one different cases of what I judged to be deliberate harm to children."

"What *you* judged… I see," said Dawkins. "I found some of your papers on the internet; however, I found no published information on the data used to determine your conclusions."

"For confidentiality reasons I had to destroy them," explained Goodwin.

"You had to destroy them… how very convenient." The note of sarcasm was clear in Dawkin's voice. "Who else routinely diagnoses F.D.I.A. on parents harming their children?"

"Several of my colleagues around the world."

"Names please, Professor Goodwin."

"I'm sorry, that is also confidential information."

"Oh, yes, I forgot its confidential!" the defence said with disdain. "You cannot give me any specific names of doctors diagnosing your invention of F.D.I.A., but it is certainly not confidential when you diagnose it in the case of Mrs Richardson!"

The prosecution was halfway up to object, when he seems to have thought better of it. He sat down again audibly tut-tutting.

"How many hours of medical consultation did you spend with Mrs Richardson in order to arrive at your diagnosis?" asked Dawkins.

"No, I didn't spend any time with Mrs Richardson," said Goodwin somewhat hesitatingly. "As I said earlier, I did a detailed study of her case notes and behaviour, with a lot of input from the prison doctor."

"Is the prison doctor a specialist in F.D.I.A.?"

"No, he's a generalist."

"How many other specialists in F.D.I.A. were able to meet Mrs Richardson to confirm your diagnosis?" insisted Dawkins.

"None, I was the only specialist involved. But believe me, as the discoverer of this disorder, I do know what to look for!" Goodwin countered defensively.

"No other second opinion?" asked Dawkins incredulously. "And you didn't even spend time with the defendant?"

Dawkins paused for effect, and then went on the attack. "Would it not be true to say that you are applying purely the fruit of your own research, and your own ideas – Goodwin's Law and F.D.I.A. – in order to come to your conclusions?"

"No, I'm not applying purely my ideas and research," retorted Goodwin. "Please do not forget that I have studied paediatrics for many decades, a discipline which encompasses the ideas of many different experts. However," he continued in his lecture voice, "my use of the cot death law and F.D.I.A. is quite legitimate for the simple reason that I am judged by my peers to be the leading expert on these particular subjects."

But Dawkins was on a roll. "And yet first you use Goodwin's law to decide that these are criminal acts and not natural accidents; and second you use the disease you discovered – F.D.I.A. – to explain away the unlikely probability of a mother deliberately killing both children. If the two babies had not died, but with the same information and NHS case notes, would you still have diagnosed Mrs Richardson with F.D.I.A.?"

"It would have been more difficult. Part of the diagnosis is her having deliberately harmed her children."

"But *only if* she harmed them," retorted Dawkins. "It seems to me Professor that you have created a self-fulfilling circular argument. She has F.D.I.A, so that's why she harmed her children. But how do we know she has F.D.I.A? Because she harmed her children. A circular argument that relies on itself to be valid is not an argument, and it's certainly way too fragile even to consider being used as proof in a court of law. And I argue diametrically the opposite – she never did have F.D.I.A., only severe depression, and she never did harm her children! Furthermore, you ignore other medical experts' opinions to make two false claims of a shaken baby for one death and smothering for another! All this just to validate your pet theory, having originally been misled by false reports of suspicious phone calls!"

"No, I beg to differ," insisted Goodwin, his voice also rising to match that of the defence barrister. "The statistics clearly speak for themselves. It's impossible that she didn't harm her children. One in 72 million, remember! How can it *not* be murder?!"

"No way!" I whispered, shaking my head violently. Actually, it was a stage whisper. My subconscious actively wanted my comment to be heard.

The judge looked sharply at me. "Juror number 6, er…" he consulted a paper, "Mr Fielding. I have already given you a warning. Do not interrupt. Do not express your opinion."

Dawkins continued. "There are quite a lot of cot deaths every year, aren't there Professor?"

Ah! I thought to myself. At last the defence is getting there! Go for it!

"Yes," replied Goodwin.

"So that is why there was no suspicion at all attached to the first death?" asked Dawkins.

"I imagine that that is the case," replied Goodwin.

"So what I want to challenge next," said Dawkins, "is indeed your statistics."

Yes, yes! I thought.

"Mrs Richardson was presumed innocent of anything

when her first child died," continued Dawkins. "So, the probability is not that of both children dying – the first one is already dead. Surely you should only use the probability of the second death happening on its own – one in 8,500 to use your figures – not one in 72 million? Very different! In April of this year we have an innocent lady, and then a one in 8,500 chance happened."

Oh... I thought. Nice try. But not really in the right direction.

"No, sir," replied Goodwin with a certain confidence. "One in 8,500 is indeed the probability of one cot death. And to follow your logic, that is why we do not lock up all the parents who suffer this tragedy. Of course, we give them the benefit of the doubt. *Once.* What changes is the *second* cot death. If you like, you can't use your get-out-of-jail-free card twice. It's cumulative, you see. For the second death it does indeed go up to one in 72 million."

I was shaking my head violently again. I got a sharp look from the judge. Stephanie put her hand on my knee to warn me. In any other situation, I would have really appreciated this gesture, but my mind was elsewhere.

"Professor, could you explain to me where you got the one in 8,500 figure from?" asked Dawkins.

"Yes," said Goodwin, "it comes from the C.E.S.D.I. study – that is 'Confidential Enquiry into Sudden Death in Infancy'. This analysed 400 sudden infant deaths in the UK over a period of three years. The report identified three main factors associated with an increased risk of death in a particular household, which were (1) the presence of smokers, (2) younger mothers under twenty-seven, and

(3) whether the household had no wage earner. In the *absence* of these three factors, which is indeed the case for the Richardsons' household, the report gives an estimate of S.I.D.S. of one in 8,543 live births, to be precise."

"But surely Professor, there is a reason for these cot deaths other than these factors?" insisted Dawkins. "Could it not be genetic – which could explain why some families suffer more than others?"

Yes, at last! I thought. I was nodding furiously. Stephanie's hand was back on my knee again to warn me. I liked its warmth; we should do more of this…

Goodwin smiled. "I was expecting this question. There is plenty of evidence that child abuse runs in families, but there is no evidence that cot deaths do." He was clearly in his stride. "Firstly, let me assure you that cot deaths are a totally random phenomenon. No one, I repeat no one, has identified any gene contributing towards them despite a lot of research. Secondly, if such a gene were to exist – which I very much doubt – it would have shown itself somewhere in the family history. As I said, I was expecting this question. That's why in the months before trial I have had a team doing extensive research into both families. We found nothing. Not one unexplained infant death. That's clear evidence of no S.I.D.S. gene, at least not in this family."

"I don't believe it!" I shouted out. "I can't believe he just said that!"

"Mr Fielding," roared the judge. "This is absolutely your last warning!"

The lead defence was looking at me quizzically, but he also

looked crestfallen. He had obviously used up the last of his ammunition and had not expected such a clear rebuttal from the witness on the question of genes. He whispered a question to his junior Hill, who just shrugged his shoulders.

"No further questions," said Dawkins, shaking his head and picking up his papers.

I just could not believe that he was not better prepared for this. At least he should put up a mathematician as another expert witness to counter these arguments.

Chapter Six

I deliberately caught the judge's eye this time. I was silently shaking my head with an incredulous look, pleading him with my eyes. With both hands doing somewhat Italian circular style movements, I was indicating towards the defence barrister to say he could not just stop there, not now!

The judge bent down and spoke to the clerk, nodding in my direction. The clerk then came over to me. "Mr Fielding, if you have a question for the judge, be so good as to write it down, but do stop interrupting and gesticulating." He did not need to ask me twice. I took one of my sheets of notepaper and quickly started writing.

"May I re-examine the witness, my Lord?" asked the prosecution.

"Just one moment please, Mr Scott," said the judge eying me.

After a few minutes I had finished writing my note:

Sir, the Professor does not even know how to use GCSE

maths. He's murdering basic probability. You need to get a mathematician to cross-examine him:

- *He's mixing up 'cause given effect' with 'effect given cause'.*
- *He should have a null hypothesis of the probability of murder to compare with the probability of two natural deaths – both unlikely events.*
- *No account taken about the sheer number of births over time.*
- *Random outcomes do NOT mean random causes.*
- *So he's assuming statistical independence when there probably is statistical dependence.*
- *"Clear evidence of no S.I.D.S. gene." You cannot prove a negative!*
- *The true odds are much, much less than one in 72 million.*

Stephanie, who was surreptitiously reading what I was writing, seemed to at least understand the first and last sentences. "Are you sure?" she whispered without moving her lips.

"Mm-hmm," I replied.

"Wow, you know no fear! Good for you!" she whispered again.

I handed the paper to the usher who carried it to the judge. The furrow on his brow got deeper as he read it.

The judge shook his head resignedly. "It seems that our juror has some questions that are very important for him," he said. "I *cannot* allow interruptions in court, but I *am* here to ensure a fair trial, and that means that the jury should have all the information they reasonably need. It's very rare, but a judge can take written questions from a member of the jury and ask them to the witness himself, if he decides the questions are appropriate. And that is now what I propose to do."

Peter Scott, QC, looked alarmingly at the judge. The judge gave him a reassuring sign, gently waving his fingers up and down while nodding his head and pursing his lips forward. Doubtless trying to convey something along the lines of 'let this young man get it out of his system before he pollutes the whole jury'.

I suddenly realised that I had not really written questions, more like observations, and rather laconic ones at that. Would the judge be able to understand what I had written? Maybe he flunked GSCE maths, or O-levels as they must have called them in his day? If only I had had the time to write out the concepts a bit clearer.

"Not sure I follow all of this," said the judge, "but let's try the first one. Professor Goodwin!"

"Yes, my Lord."

"Are you mixing up 'cause given effect' with 'effect given cause'?"

"Pardon, my Lord. This sounds like semantics. I really don't understand the question."

I was visibly shaking my head in a dispirited and desperate manner.

The judge scowled at me. "Neither do I, really, I'm afraid," he said. "Let's try the next one. Do you have a hypothesis for the probability of murder?"

I audibly groaned at the way the judge was now murdering my question. Did he deliberately exclude the word 'null'? Why didn't he read the whole sentence? The judge looked at me, perplexed.

"But that is exactly what I have been saying since the beginning, my Lord," answered Goodwin to the judge's modified version of my question. "For statistical reasons, the only possible hypothesis is that of murder."

Again, I was shaking my head.

"Hmmm," said the judge, "I really don't understand these questions."

"I'm not sure the juror does either, sir," added Goodwin, ever trying to be helpful.

The prosecution had got to his feet. "May I suggest, my Lord, that we move along? I'm sure Mr Fielding will have plenty of time to discuss these questions with his fellow jurors later on."

The judge seemed to come to a decision. "I have a proposal to make. But first I need to consult with counsel. For that I must ask the usher to clear the jury from the court. It won't be for long."

We all trooped out and went to the jury room.

I pieced together the discussion that took place in our absence from certain sources that I shall keep confidential.

Once we had gone, the judge called the prosecution and defence barristers forward. Apparently, nobody else could really hear what they were saying. "The pertinence of your expert witness' testimony resides not only in his mastery of statistics but that he is *seen* to master statistics," the judge said to Scott and Sturdee. "And given that Mr Fielding has publicly made what might well be an erroneous assertation, so that there might be no doubt in the rest of the jury's mind, I will ask Mr Fielding to ask and explain his questions himself."

Peter Scott, QC, was almost apoplectic. "I really must object, my Lord! This is totally unprecedented."

"Well then, please expose your arguments."

"My Lord, this is really over the top," replied Scott. "A young jury member thinks he knows better than our esteemed expert. He insults him. You permit him to write down questions nobody understands, least of all our expert. *Now* you invite him to ask his questions directly. This has never happened in a court of law and should never be allowed to happen. Professional barristers ask the questions, jury members listen and decide later. If the jury starts intervening and cross-examining a key witness, his or her objectivity is immediately compromised, without talking about the impact on the other jurors. Whatever the result of this trial, you are opening the doors for an appeal to quash the verdict." Sturdee was looking similarly angry.

The judge turned to the defence, "Mr Dawkins, Mr Hill, do either of you wish to comment?"

"My Lord, this is most unusual," said Dawkins. "Normally it is our job to find any faults in the prosecution expert witness' testimony. But I would never let my pride get in the way of helping our client to a fair trial. If this young juror can uncover inconsistencies that we have not seen, we are only too willing to let him have a crack at it." Hill was nodding his assent.

"Thank you, Mr Dawkins," replied the judge. "Mr Scott, Mr Sturdee, I fully appreciate the precedence that this creates. Let other, future, judges decide whether this is a mistake or new jurisprudence. Meanwhile, although I note your objections, seeing as I have already opened the door to Pandora's box, I feel I have to go the whole way. I have *already* decided to let this juror's questions be aired by asking him for a list for me to read out; however, since no one seems to understand his questions, and given that these statistics seem to be the fundamental core for the prosecution's arguments, I thus choose to ask him to explain the questions himself, and I'm sure Professor Goodwin will correct any misunderstandings. My decision rests."

After fifteen minutes outside, we were invited back in. The two prosecution barristers were visibly sulking. The two defence councils, and the defence solicitor, were all smiling.

The judge addressed the jury. "Ladies and gentlemen, you are going to witness a legal precedent. As far as I know, this is the first time ever where the judge, that is me, is going to invite a jury member to ask his own questions directly to the witness."

There was an audible murmur around the courtroom.

"For the record," continued the judge, "I do this because Professor Goodwin's testimony seems to be the key element for the prosecution's case. He is using statistical concepts that only one person so far has shown any apparent mathematical ability to challenge, juror number 6, Mr Fielding. Normally it is my job to ask any necessary questions from a juror, which is in itself an exceptional event. But I admit freely that I do not understand all these questions. I wish this to be a fair trial. Also, for the record, while the defence counsel has no objection to this action, the prosecution counsel has voiced his objection. However, this is the decision I have made."

He turned to me. "Mr Fielding, you had better demonstrate that you master this subject, or I will stop you immediately. Please ask your questions to the witness, Professor Goodwin, whom I require to answer. Please do take the time necessary to explain to the court any of your reasonings. I do also invite the witness to challenge your reasoning as necessary. Look upon this as two experts challenging each other."

So that is how I came to be in this unimaginable situation. As I digested those different looks both killing me and pleading with me, my mind simultaneously took in the enormity of it. Here I was, a nervous twenty-six-year-old engineer about to create legal history by being invited, as a member of the jury, to directly cross-examine one of the country's leading paediatricians, the prosecution's main witness, to boot; and all this during a murder trial in the Old Bailey. But surely, I can't be the only person here who understands statistics?

With all eyes looking at me, I stammered out my first question. "Pr-Professor Goodwin, you say that there is only a one in 72 million chance that Mrs Richardson's children died of natural causes?"

"Yes, that is exactly what I said. Very clearly and several times."

"So, if I am to understand from your statement," I continued a little bit more confidently, "the accused was chosen purely at random, pulled in off the street if you like, and *only then* was it discovered that two of her babies had died in succession?"

"Don't be ridiculous, young man!" retorted Goodwin.

"We all know Mrs Richardson was arrested for murder precisely because her baby boys had died."

"I agree with the witness, my Lord," shouted the prosecution. "This is ridiculous. Must we really go on?"

"Mr Fielding," interrupted the judge, "please get to the point and do not treat the court to facetious remarks."

"My Lord. From a mathematical point of view, Professor Goodwin's statement is exactly as if she *were* pulled in off the street at random," I replied.

"Well, you had better get on with it and explain yourself then."

"Professor, please explain again how you reached your calculation."

"I repeat, *again*: there is a one in 8,500 chance of the first death being a cot death multiplied by one in 8,500 for the second, thus one in 72 million. Statistically impossible to happen by accident. It had to be murder."

"But how many births are there in the UK every year?" I asked.

"About 800,000," he replied.

I was beginning to enjoy this. "So, within a time frame of, say, ten years – since fortunately we don't often hear about double baby murders – we could, conceptually, have pulled in from the streets ten times 800,000, that's 8 million women, who have recently given birth. Let's say half of them, 4 million, were second or third births. Then we ask them if two of their babies had died in a row? And yes, it so happens that one of them, Mrs Richardson, fits that profile. My point is that we had 4 million different chances to find someone guilty. So, Professor Goodwin, your probability is not one in 72 million, it's one in 72 million divided by 4 million which is exactly one in eighteen. Not one in eighteen hundred or one eighteen thousand, but one in eighteen!"

"But for her individually, the probability is indeed one in 72 million!" Goodwin countered.

I was theatrically shaking my head. "Professor Goodwin, I think we can all agree that we did *not* pull Mrs Richardson in off the street at random. She is sitting accused in this court, out of all the millions of mothers giving birth, *precisely* because a rare event happened to her. Let me illustrate this with another question. If 50 million people bought a lottery ticket, and one of them won the £30 million prize, would you have him arrested because he only had a one in 50 million chance of winning and thus must have cheated?"

"No, of course not, somebody had to win."

"Yes, *somebody* had to win the lottery, and there were 50 million independent tries to do so. Precisely. Like in our case, 4 million second babies being born."

"But even with your warped logic," said Goodwin defensively, "it was still only a one in 18 chance of those being natural deaths. I don't believe in coincidences."

"My logic is not warped," I countered, "it is the *correct* statistical treatment of your very own data and your own premises. And believe me, I will be questioning these next. You simply forgot to take into account the sheer number of events. Yes, with *your* data, *if* it were correct, an *individual* may only have a one in 72 million chance of witnessing a double tragedy, but you completely ignored that over ten years there are 4 million second births in Britain, so 4 million chances for different individuals to experience this tragic rare event. As a result, we are down from your incorrectly stated proof of one in 72 million, to only one in 18, a full six per cent chance of having bad luck. And who says you can predict exactly when and where a rare bad luck event is going to happen? For example, how many births are there in the *world* per year, Professor Goodwin?"

"I don't know."

"Do you have your phone on you?"

"Yes."

I turned to the judge. "My Lord, may I ask the witness to go on Google to get this information?"

"Yes, you may," he answered.

"Professor, please Google the number of births in the world each year."

Goodwin, pulled out his phone, went onto his Google app, typed in a few key words and then selected the link that came up and scrolled down. "Let me see. It says there are 131 million births per year worldwide."

"So," I continued, "it seems that every year, again using your very own *questionable* numbers, there would be 131 divided by two, that's about 66 million births a year of second, or third or more, babies, divided by 72 million, almost one case of double cot deaths per year, or about nine cases over our ten-year period. OK, statistically this is more likely to happen in highly populated countries like China or India. But who are you to say, Professor Goodwin, that this cannot happen in Britain?"

"But," insisted Goodwin, "you're forgetting the corroborative evidence – the marks that suggest smothering."

"Is it probable that an innocent mother, with advanced first-aid training, would try to resuscitate her baby if she sees he is no longer breathing?"

"Yes, I suppose so."

"Can you *prove* to the court that those marks were *not* made by the mother trying to resuscitate her child?" I was beginning to sound just like one of these lawyers.

"No," admitted Goodwin, "but it is strong corroborative evidence against her; I personally am convinced it was smothering."

"What is more likely," I asked, "that a mother tries to resuscitate her child, or that a mother deliberately kills her child?"

Mr Scott, QC, was on his feet again. "My Lord, the juror is asking a rhetorical question!"

"I agree," said the judge. "Mr Fielding, be more careful. I assume you wish to ask your other questions?"

"Yes, indeed I do, my Lord."

"Well then, we will break the court at this juncture. Tomorrow you may continue to ask your questions to Professor Goodwin. But I warn you, Mr Fielding, to be very careful in your insinuations and to avoid your flippant remarks. Otherwise, I *will* shut you down. Do you understand?"

"Yes, my Lord."

"The court is adjourned."

Everyone followed the court clerk's lead of getting to their feet. The judge stood up and then disappeared in his funny wig, one without curlers on it.

Chapter Seven

We jurors were led out to the jury room by our two jury keepers. They said we were free to leave whenever we wanted too. They also told us to leave any notes taken inside the jury room, and they provided us with a stack of card folders with our jury numbers on the front to put them in.

But nobody was in a hurry to leave; suddenly it seemed that everybody was talking at the same time. Most seemed to disapprove of my actions.

"Our job is to listen, not to interrupt. What the hell do you think you are doing?" commented one.

"Do you really think at your age you know more than this guy who's published more than 200 papers? Trying to be the hero, are you?" asked another.

"If that mother 'as murdered 'er sons, she deserves to be put away, and it's not your job to undermine the prosecution with airy fairy questions. I agree, it's our job to listen," said a third.

"I've never heard of a judge letting a member of the jury ask questions directly to a witness," said another. "I'm not even sure he's allowed to do that. This will probably result in a mis-trial."

Finally, there was one relatively positive comment from one of the more middle-aged jurors, "There's something about that professor's superior attitude I don't like; at least you put him in his place!"

The appointed foreperson spoke out. I remember thinking, what do we call her? Madame Foreman, or Madame Foreperson? In the end we just called her by her first name, Hilary. "Do we want to rapidly debrief this evening, or do you wish to leave?" she asked. The consensus was that we could all spare a few minutes to discuss, so we sat down at the large oval table.

"Who wants to go first?" asked Hilary.

One of the business suits answered. "I'd like to know what was in the list that Fielding – sorry what was your first name again…?"

"Martin."

"…that Martin here gave to the judge." Several others agreed.

So, I told them line by line what I had written.

"I'm afraid that goes over my head," said one of the bus drivers' brigade.

"Me too," said another.

Business suit carried on. "I can guess what you're trying to get at on some of those points. But just reassure me. Do you actually know what you are talking about?"

"Yes, it's only basic GCSE maths."

"I did maths to GCSE and got a B, but still I'm not sure I understand. How come you're such a hotshot then?"

"Well, I had to do a lot of maths for four years at university as part of my engineering degree, and then a fifth year for my MSc." I then explained how wave analysis for offshore engineering was largely based on statistical probability concepts. "So, although I'm not a statistician, I do have a good grounding in the subject."

"Are you really saying that this professor is telling porkies?" asked another.

"I don't think he is deliberately," I replied. "Generally, doctors study maths to A-level only – and then not all. Afterwards they are in their own medical world of how the body functions, diseases, surgery, you name it. This guy did his A-levels well over forty years ago. He probably never had to learn probability from first principles like I had to, and if he did, he's probably forgotten it. I think he believes what he's saying, it's just that he's missing out some key elements."

"What would those be, then?" asked someone.

"Well, they're on my list. I think the main one he's missing is statistical dependence rather than independence. If a cot death has already happened, who's to say it's not more likely to happen again? That's one of the key questions I will ask him tomorrow. He said there was clear evidence of no cot death gene. That is semantical bullshit. You just can't say that."

Some people round the table looked dubious. "I'd have thought he would know more about genes than you do!" said one.

"Yes," I said, "but it seems I know more about maths, and right now that's more important."

"Your funeral!"

Hilary fore-whatsit took back the lead. "Personally, I'm whacked, so I would like to head home. Maybe we should all just listen to Martin's questions tomorrow, and then listen to Professor Goodwin's responses. After that we might be a little wiser."

"Sounds like a plan!"

"Yup, good idea."

"See you tomorrow!"

So, we got up, knocked on the door to summon our babysitters, and started leaving the room. Soon people had gathered their smartphones from their lockers, and suddenly they were busy answering extremely important messages and emails. Or was it just cat pictures on Instagram?

"Thanks for your moral support," I said to Stephanie on the way out. "It was just what I needed. I was really nervous."

"Yes, I could see. You did pretty well; you're going up against an icon of the medical profession – I'm impressed! But you need to watch yourself, you must have better control of your outbursts or comments. If the judge shuts you down, your questions won't be answered."

"I guess you're right. Fancy a drink? I could murder a pint!"

"Me to. Let's find a nearby pub."

As we came out of the building, two photographers took our photo.

"That looks ominous," I said to Stephanie. Fortunately, they did not follow us, and we soon found ourselves in the Magpie and Stump down a little cobbled street right opposite the Old Bailey's entrance. Although it was only early evening, there were already a lot of lawyer types around us, obviously one of the favourite watering holes for the Central Criminal Court.

"Hope we don't bump into the prosecution team," I said. "They would probably lace my beer with arsenic."

"Then they would become the defendants and claim that it is statistically probable that you died a natural death!"

I bought a couple of pints of real ale chosen at random amongst the large choice available along the bar counter. (Ah but, I thought, it never is totally random, is it?) I also chose two packets of cheese and onion crisps (my favourite flavour, therefore not random).

"Cheers!" I said.

"Cheers!" We both drank heartily.

"Oh, I forgot," I added, "Montignac strictly forbids beers in his diet, too many carbohydrates. That's why he likes wine."

"Maybe that's because he's French?" suggested Stephanie. "So, you like waves, do you? Both the offshore and onshore variety?"

"Onshore?" I looked into my beer to see if in my thirst I had created a tidal wave.

"Yes. You certainly made waves in the courtroom today! And you've made waves with most of the rest of the jury – they gave you a lot of flak tonight. I guess that 'one in 72 million' chance of it not being a murder got to them. They've already decided she's guilty and so nobody should pick holes."

"Who needs facts when opinions and prejudice are much more fun?" I joked. "Just look at the Brexit referendum or Trump's election. Or worse, look at what has happened since. I don't know if they've already made up their mind –

if so, my job will be to get this Professor Goodwin to admit he's made a mistake and so convince them otherwise. I think the real problem is that they don't like a young upstart like me getting above his station, so to speak. The French have a wonderful and rather crude expression for that, which I could roughly and slightly more elegantly translate as 'breaking wind above your rear posterior'."

"I'm a nurse, used to some very crude language. You don't have to put any gloves on for me!"

"OK, the literal translation is 'farting above your ass'."

"I like it. I'm going to remember that one! You seem to refer to the French rather a lot. Why?"

"I did a three-month summer internship for a French offshore engineering company in Paris."

"I didn't know they had any oil in France."

"They don't really. They just follow Total around the world. They also do a lot of work for the American oil companies. They like the excuse to come to Paris for technical meetings. It was part of my job to look after some American clients when they came over and accompany them to the Moulin Rouge for the second part of the meetings."

"Too much information!" she said, laughing. "So, what did you all get up to in the Moulin Rouge?"

"Nothing too untoward. The American clients were all shocked at the dancers' bare breasts. No, I think thrilled would be a better word. We did almost lose the next stage of the contract, though."

"How?"

"I'll tell you once I refill our glasses." Which I did, and paid for again, being the perfect gentleman with only a few ulterior motives.

73

We tucked into our second pints.

"So, was it the bare breasts that almost scuppered your contract?" she asked.

"No, I'm sure that encouraged them to stick with us!" I said. "What happened is that we made our client look a fool, literally. We'd booked well ahead and had paid extra for one of the best tables, which means we were right next to the central stage that sticks out into the dining area. This comedian comes on between two dances. He says he needs volunteers. But he selects the volunteers himself, and there he is pulling our client's top man up onto the stage. He gets another two victims from other tables and sets the three of them up as ventriloquist dummies. It's all done in English for the tourists. Whenever he squeezes one of them on the arm, that person has to open and close his mouth, while the comedian adds the words. Well, the other two were staged as having an argument, and every now and then they would ask our guy for his opinion. He opens and closes his mouth a few times, but all that seems to come out of are the grunting sounds of a mentally challenged idiot. It was actually very funny, and our client's colleagues were rolling about laughing to see their boss that way. But our man did not appreciate it at all." I took another swig of my beer.

"Anyway, next day we won him back," I continued, "not so much with all our brilliant technical presentations, but more in the company restaurant."

"What, the gourmet French food?" she asked.

"No, something a bit more down to earth," I said. "You see, the ground floor of our office building was an in-house self-service restaurant, together with a couple of VIP rooms where you actually get served, the food's more upmarket and

74

there are some pretty good wines. Well, to begin with, this same VIP, he's shocked we serve alcohol on the premises. He explained how this would be a firing offence in the States: any alcohol consumed at work, and you're out. But after his second glass of Saint-Emilion he was actually coming around to the idea that maybe France wasn't such a heathen place after all. But what really made him delighted was when one of the French team explained to him how to impress his friends back home by becoming an instant wine expert." I paused to de-ballast my glass a little more. Why does it go down so fast?

"And how do you that?"

"It's very easy, as my colleague explained to him. If French wines are being served – he should make sure the wines are French and not from some other country – he should check if the bottle has shoulders on it. If so, he should pour a little into his glass, swirl it around, hold it up to the light, deeply inhale the delicate bouquet, sip it and swirl it around the mouth, make some rather rude sounding slurping noises, swallow, nod sagely, and then he should calmly announce to his friends that this wine must come from Bordeaux. The friends will of course be impressed by his expertise but wouldn't necessarily believe him. So, they all look up 'Chateau Haut-Paullac' or 'Saint-Emilion Cru Bourgeois' on Google Maps, and are astonished to find it right next to Bordeaux."

"OK," she said, "but there are so many different wine Chateaux in France, how is he supposed to know which ones come from Bordeaux?"

"It's simply the shoulders on the bottle." I explained. "In France, only the Bordeaux wines come in bottles with shoulders, as opposed to bottles with a smoother more rounded curve for the other regions. There are some exceptions, Côte de Provence, which is further East, that also comes in bottles with shoulders, but you'd be unlikely to find this exported to the USA. Anyway, people love to imagine they are wine snobs, and they love even more to be able impress their friends. So, this wonderful pearl of wisdom won back the head and heart of our client. He spent the rest of the meal happily swirling wine around in his mouth and shouting, 'It's Bordeaux!'"

"I'm going to try that one with some of my nursing friends!" said Stephanie, laughing.

"Anyway, after our boozy lunch, he approved the funding for the next part of our project. As he was signing, he was proud to tell us that his company strictly forbade anyone to sign contracts after having been taken out to a meal with alcohol served – can't think why – but then, he said, we wouldn't tell, would we?

"Let's talk about your job," I said, changing the subject. "Do you enjoy intensive care?"

"Yes," she said. "It's full of action. Never a boring moment. Hardly a shift goes by without some emergency to handle."

"You said they were mostly heart patients?"

"Yes, in my ward. The most critical time is of course the heart surgery itself, but the next most critical is the intensive care while they recover afterwards."

"Do you ever lose any patients?"

"We try not to. I have found myself ripping open the sutures and pumping a stopped heart with my own hands, while the alarm goes for the crash team to arrive."

"Wow! Did you save him?"

"Yes. But some of the others I couldn't," she said sadly.

I placed my hand on hers. "I don't know how you live with such a stress. I admire you."

"Thanks," she said as she gently pulled her hand out from under mine. "Of course, it's heart disease that's the killer, just as bad as cancer. We do our best, but it sometimes just isn't enough."

I tried to lighten the mood with a rather macabre joke. "Well, if you've had two or more die on you, I promise not to tell Professor Goodwin. He'll have the whole lot of you in court!"

We finished our beers.

I rather nervously asked her if I could invite her out to dinner, maybe grab some pub food here? She said it was very sweet of me, but that it had already been a full day, and she had better be going since she had things to do back in her flat.

"May I have your phone number?"

"Yes." She smiled, and gave it to me.

I typed it into my phone and rang her. "Now you've got my number, too," I said as her phone buzzed.

"See you tomorrow," she said as she pecked me on the cheek. I liked that.

We went our different ways once outside. I wondered where her flat was. Wishful thinking! She probably has a steady boyfriend.

Sitting on the tube, images of Stephanie faded from my two-pint mind, to be replaced by the vision of Professor

Goodwin humiliating me the next day and then the judge throwing me out of court. I like a challenge, and in the face of problems, I look for solutions; that's the way I'm wired! At least, that is what I told myself. It seemed to do the trick, by the time I got off at Tooting Bec Station, I already had some ideas to follow up.

While nibbling some stale bread and cheese, doubtless with Montignac turning in his grave, I checked some ideas by surfing on the internet. I considered that I was not committing a crime, firstly because they specifically wanted me to ask questions that were correct, and secondly, I was not researching the case, just revising mathematical probability concepts. I also pulled out Taleb's book *The Black Swan*, to check on the section where he writes about random causes and random results. I found quite a few other ideas in there too.

I noted some angles of attack for my questions the next day. I hoped the ushers would let me take the paper into the courtroom. Although the ideas were pretty well imprinted in my mind, I knew from experience that when standing up to give a presentation to clients, if I did not have written bullet points to remind me, the sheer nervousness of talking to a room full of people leads you to forget half of what you want to say.

I did not sleep very well that night. Sometimes fully alert, sometimes in the neverland between consciousness and sleep, I was already continuing my cross-examination. Twice I sat up and added some more ideas to my list for the next day. At one point I had to will myself to calm down in order to get to sleep, just like I used to do before exams. The fact that you cannot sleep makes you even more worked up, so that then you certainly cannot sleep. You just have to tell yourself that it's actually not that important, that whatever happens the next day, even if you don't sleep at all, it really doesn't matter, you'll still do OK. It worked; I finally slipped off into a fitful sleep.

Chapter Eight

Next morning, at ten minutes to ten, all the jurors were in the jury room, all feeling distinctly naked without any mobile phones, but ready to go. Despite my lack of sleep, it seemed my adrenalin was keeping me wide awake and alert, at least for the time being. So at least I did not have to drink too much coffee; can you imagine having to ask the judge for a loo break?

"Did you see the newspaper headlines this morning?" asked one of my fellow jurors. "'72 million to one its murder, says expert' – that was in *The Times*."

"*The Sun* has a picture of our young would-be Einstein and the girl, coming out of the courthouse," said another. "The caption says, 'Mad judge lets young juror cross-examine'. It goes on to say that the British justice system must be scraping the bottom of the barrel if any Tom, Dick and Harry can interrupt critical expert testimony, or something like that."

"We must not read or be influenced by the press," said

Hilary. "I avoided buying or reading any papers exactly for that reason. I did not look up any reporting on my phone either. I suggest you all do the same."

The jury keeper came in, smiled, and then filed us out into the courtroom for the second day of questioning witnesses.

As I was taking my place in the jury box, Stephanie whispered to me, "Go for it! You can do it. Break wind!" I could not suppress a giggle at the thought of some embarrassing sound happening just as there was perfect silence in the courtroom.

We all stood up as the judge came in. He looked carefully around the courtroom, first at the jury box, then to the public seats; he smiled.

"Good morning," he said, as we all sat down with him. "Let's get to work. Please bring in Professor Goodwin."

Once the usher had installed him in the witness stand, the judge continued. "Good morning, Professor Goodwin, I remind you that you are still under oath." He turned to me. "Mr Fielding, please do stand up and carry on with your questions. And I ask you not to get out of line. If you do, I will stop you. Is that clear?"

"Yes, my Lord." I cleared my throat, and looked at my notes that the jury keeper had indeed allowed me to take in. "Professor, first I would like to understand your figure of one in 8,500 as the average for cot deaths. You said this was from a study of 400 cot deaths over three years, and this figure applies to families that are non-smoking, have a wage earner and the mother is over twenty-seven?"

"Yes, that is correct," he answered.

"What are the odds if some of these conditions don't apply?"

Goodwin shuffled through some papers he had brought with him. "Yes, as we said, for the case where none of the aggravating factors are present – smoking, unemployment, young mothers – the probability is indeed one S.I.D.S. for every 8,543 live births. If one of the factors is present, this reduces to one in 1,616 live births."

"What?!" I exclaim. "If there is *either* a smoker in the house, *or* if both parents are unemployed, *or* if the mother is young, suddenly the odds of a cot death are – what…" I did some quick mental calculations, "…more than five times more likely?"

"Yes, about that."

"What happens when there are two, or all three, of these factors present?"

"With two aggravating factors present, the odds are one in 596," said Goodwin looking at his paper. "If all three factors are present, the odds are one in 214."

"One in 214 compared with one in 8,500?!" I did another bit of mental arithmetic. "About 40 times more likely to happen than your statistic for the defendant?!"

"Yes," said Goodwin, "but none of those aggravating factors were present. I repeat, none. So, the one in 8,500 is the correct figure to use."

"But if we use the one in 214 figure instead, the probability of a random succession of two cot deaths would be one in 214 squared…" in my mind I squared the 2 and then added two lots of two zeros, "a bit more than one in only 40,000 – a lot less than one in 72 million! Then, if there are 400,000 second or more births each year, and if, just for the sake of argument, all parents were smokers, unemployed and young, then 400,000 divided by 40,000 would give us

10 double cot deaths per year. Mrs Richardson would never be in court. Is her crime simply because she doesn't smoke, she's over twenty-seven and that she or her husband have a job?"

"Don't be flippant!" Goodwin shot back at me angrily. "The figures for her category are clearly one in 8,500, not one in 214."

I also caught a look of disapproval from the judge.

"But just look at the variability," I countered. "You just change one or more small variable in the baby's environment, and your figure comes tumbling down to much higher odds of cot deaths. What was the aim of this study?"

"To identify families at higher risks than others," answered Goowin. "Once warned, we can use better baby surveillance methods, like apnoea alarms and so on."

"So, it's *descriptive* to identify risks," I said. "Since when does descriptive become *prescriptive*? The defendant does not have the right to have more cot deaths simply because her husband works?"

Unsurprisingly, Goodwin chose not to answer my rhetorical question.

I decided to change tack slightly. "This is based on an analysis of 400 cot deaths, you say?"

"Yes."

"What defines a cot death?"

"When a young infant dies of no known cause," replied Goodwin.

"No known cause... or perhaps a cause which is known but that is just not visible?" I asked.

"Well, yes. That would apply as well."

"So," I said, "it's a bit arbitrary. Some well-known natural cause is not found, because the body hides the symptoms, or because the pathologist does not have enough experience in baby post-mortems, so it gets qualified as a cot death. If on the other hand, the cause is visible, it gets qualified as something else. I suppose the full number of infant deaths is much higher."

"If you include infections, known pathologies and so on, yes," he replied.

"So, if we said, 'death by all natural causes' and not just 'cot deaths', we would have more deaths, so more than one in 8,500 in your extreme best-case environment, and more than one in 214 at the other extreme for the worst-case environment?"

"Er, yes," he concurred.

"So, you're penalising Mrs Richardson, using harsher odds against natural deaths, not only because of no smoking, having jobs and being over twenty-seven, but also, perhaps, because the pathologist didn't do his job well enough?"

Again, no reply.

I decided to open yet another door of weakness in his arguments. "In your opinion," I said, "is 400 cases over three years a big enough sample, and a big enough time span, to get accurate probabilities?

"Yes, I think it's pretty good."

"Wait, you identified three variables," I countered. "That means you have three squared, that's nine possible combinations of each variable – none of them, one of them (but which one?), two of them (again which two?) or all of them. That's 400 divided by nine, about 44 cases of cot death for each combination of variables. That's not enough data to identify clear trends. A few unusual happenings could corrupt events – maybe there was temporarily milder weather, so less flu virus going around at that time, just as an example. And who says that what happens in one period of three years is representative of what happens a few years later?"

Liking the sound of my own voice, I ploughed on. "Let's take an example from my own experience – my company designs offshore oil platforms. We did *hundreds of thousands* of wave height measurements where a platform was to be installed in the North Sea. We extrapolated the data to get the so-called one-hundred-year wave – the big one that comes on average every hundred years, so that we can design the platform to withstand it. But once the platform was installed, lo and behold, waves bigger than the hundred-year-wave hit the platform *twice* in the first five years and did extensive damage. In your opinion what went wrong?"

"I really know nothing about waves and oil platforms; I am a *doctor*," replied Goodwin dryly. "But I presume you made a mistake in your calculations."

"Yes, you are a doctor, sir," I said. "And from what I see you are definitely not a mathematician!"

"Careful, Mr Fielding," said the judge.

"My Lord," I replied, "although I do not have any legal training, I am given to understand that an expert witness should only give evidence in his area of expertise. Would you as a judge accept me, an engineer, to give, say, expert medical evidence on infections discovered in pathological post-mortems?"

The judge visibly bridled. "Under your own admission

you do not have any legal training, Mr Fielding, so you are *not* a qualified lawyer and even *less* a qualified judge. Please leave your comments on interpreting the law, and who can say what in my courtroom, to me. Meanwhile, get on with it, and explain why your oil platform red herring is relevant to this witness' testimony!"

Turning back to Goodwin, I said, "No, our calculations were accurate. It was the *data samples that were wrong*, or perhaps insufficient. Either the length of time we used to sample wave height was too short, or during that period some random external effect was present – maybe the moon calmed the waters, or some atmospheric condition corrupted the sampling, we will never know."

"What's your point, young man?" Goodwin demanded impatiently. The prosecution was nodding vigorously to mirror Goodwin's impatience.

"My point," I said, "is that *your* cot death data is not reasonably reliable. Why? Because the chances of a baby's death happening goes up if we include *all* natural deaths, and not just those we can't identify. Because only 44 data points for any given combination of variables is just not enough to determine reliable statistics. Because you mistake *description* for *prescription*. Because we see an enormous variability with just a few changes in innocent variables. And maybe it's not these variables that really change the probability – cot deaths may be due to some other factors that are simply found more often along with, say, unemployed parents or younger mothers; and perhaps these other factors are also present in the Richardson's household despite the parents' employment or despite the mother being a bit older. And finally, you have fallen for the '*ecological fallacy*'."

"What on earth is that?" asked Goodwin. The expression on the judge's face seemed to agree with Godwin's exasperation.

"It's when you fall into the trap of assuming that the *average* of a population applies to *each individual* in that population. There is an incredible variation of probabilities within any population, your *own* data proves this. Nobody is average, there will always be individual extremes that average out. It's not a crime to be different from the average, it's normal.

"For example, Professor. Would you cross a river that is four feet deep *on average*?" There was subdued laughter around the courtroom as what I had said sunk in. "No, I thought not. The Richardson's household might have only one in 8,500 chances of having a cot death *on average*; but the actual *individual probability* for the Richardsons could be very different; your very own data shows that you tweak a few variables and the odds shoot up to one in 200."

The judge decided we all needed a break, or at least he needed one. After he had left, we filed out to the jury room.

My fellow jurors were slightly more muted this morning and seemed more interested in grabbing a quick coffee rather than talking to me. Maybe I had laboured the point too much on averages not applying to individuals, and I doubted whether that had really swayed their prejudices. I guessed 'the jury was out' – in all its meanings – as to whether they thought I actually knew what I was talking about.

When we came back in twenty minutes later, I decided to attack from an even more important angle.

Chapter Nine

"Professor Goodwin," I said, "what are the statistics of a mother murdering her own baby? What is the probability?"

"I don't have this exact information."

"What, you don't have this information?" I asked, trying to sound incredulous.

"No."

"In your opinion," I said, "is it more likely that a baby dies of a cot death, or that a baby is murdered by its mother?"

"Fortunately, murder is quite rare," he replied. "So, for a *single* death it's more likely to be S.I.D.S. It's for *double* deaths that murder becomes the more likely scenario."

"What, then, are the statistics of mothers murdering two of their babies in a row, Professor?"

"I don't have this information either. But in any case, you can't simply multiply the probabilities for single murders. You see, a person diagnosed with F.D.I.A. is much more likely to commit murder than someone who is not, and that same higher probability applies to the second murder. The events are statistically dependant."

"*Statistically dependent?*" I repeated with emphasis. "Very interesting and very important concept. We will come back to this. But in any case, you couldn't multiply the probabilities even if you wanted to, because you don't have them in the first place!"

I caught another warning glance from the judge.

I moved on. "Have you heard of the '*prosecutor's fallacy*', Professor Goodwin?"

"No, I don't believe I have. But doubtless you are going to enlighten me…" he said, rolling his eyes upwards. It seemed to me that Mr Scott was doing the same.

"It's when you confuse 'cause given effect' with 'effect given cause'."

Goodwin was shaking his head. "As I said when the judge asked me that question yesterday, it sounds like semantics to me."

"Oh no," I shot back. "It's not semantics. We know the 'effect' – two of Mrs Richardson's children have died. The court's role is to determine the *cause* of this effect, given that this rare event has actually already happened. However unlikely it was, it *has* happened. We should now analyse *all* the causes: natural, murder; maybe something else. And we should compare the *probabilities* of *each* cause to see which is the most likely, even if all of them have only a small chance of happening. It's the *relative* probabilities that count, *not* the *absolute* probabilities. For arguments sake, let's say double cot deaths have one chance in a million of happening, but double murder has one chance in ten million: they are both extremely unlikely. But the unlikely has happened, and by comparing the *two* probabilities, we see that natural deaths are, in this example, more likely than murder. 'Cause given effect'.

"But you, Professor," I continued, "have only been analysing *one* cause, cot deaths, for the purpose of eliminating it. You come up with a very small probability. (I believe you calculated wrongly, but we'll come back to that.) You calculated a probability so small that you immediately jumped to the conclusion that it is murder *without* even trying to calculate and *compare* with the *probability* of murder. 'Effect given cause'. The 'effect' – double deaths – given the 'cause' – S.I.D.S. – is you think so unlikely to happen that you unilaterally eliminate it as a possibility."

"I'm not really sure I fully follow you," said Goodwin trying to sound as confused as possible.

"I think you do," I said.

I tried a parallel example. "Surely as an experienced medical researcher you know that all hypotheses have to be tested against a second null hypothesis?"

"Of course, I do believe that I know more about medical research than you do, young man!"

"But *where* are the *two* hypotheses, Professor? You need to compare the probability of an unlikely event of two cot deaths with the null hypothesis of the probability of another unlikely event of double murder? I only see one set of analysis. You yourself surprised me just now by saying you did not even know the probabilities of murder.

"Only if the *probability* of double cot deaths is much, much *less* likely than the *probability* of double murder,"

I continued, "can you then say that there is a statistical probability of murder. But you didn't even analyse the probability of murder. You willingly admit that a single cot death is more likely than a mother murdering one child. However, then you assume that double cot deaths are so unlikely, that you simply jump to the conclusion that it therefore had to double be murder! Not very scientific…"

The prosecution was jumping to his feet. "I really cannot accept that these comments go to the witness' character!"

"Mr Fielding," interrupted the judge. "I will not have you making any insinuations against the esteemed professor. I must confess you have also completely lost me in what seem to be useless semantics. I think we will stop your…" The judge stopped in mid-sentence. He seemed to be glaring at someone in the public gallery over to his far left. A look of resignation came over his face. "Oh, very well. On second thoughts, you may continue your questioning. But please ask simple questions, stick to facts and avoid giving your opinion."

"My apologies, sir," I said. "I will try to rephrase and simplify. Professor Goodwin. When testing a new drug in clinical trials, do you check for the possible effects of the drug against a null hypothesis of the same effects happening by chance. That is do you administer the drug to half the test population and administer a placebo to the other half?"

"Yes, that is the normal procedure."

"In this case did you check and compare the probabilities of both hypotheses? Natural deaths and murder?"

"Er, no. The probability of natural deaths is so small that it wasn't necessary. It was obviously murder," affirmed Goodwin.

"'It wasn't necessary'," I repeated incredulously. "You just waived standard scientific protocol of analysing the *two* probabilities. 'Obviously', you say. Obvious to you, perhaps? But not to me. Did you not just admit that murder, let alone double murder, was also a very rare event?"

"Er, yes, I did," he admitted.

"And did we not conclude, even using *your* statistics – which I am going to question in a minute – that due to the sheer number of births there is probably at least one set of double cot deaths per year happening by accident somewhere in the world?"

"Yes, we did. In the world, perhaps; but not in Britain," Goodwin added rather churlishly.

I paused to review my notes from the small hours of the night. "Let us come to what is going to be the most important part of our analysis together. The likelihood of a double event. Professor Goodwin, just now you said that someone who had already committed murder was more likely than someone else to commit murder again?"

"Yes indeed, a person diagnosed with F.D.I.A. is much more likely to commit murder than someone who is not, and that same high probability applies to the second murder."

"So you confirm what you said earlier, the events are *statistically dependant*?" I asked.

"Yes," he said nodding.

"So, for the double murder possibility, you insist on it not being two independent random events. That once a murderer, there is much more chance of again being a murderer?"

"Yes."

"Now, for cot deaths, or S.I.D.S., you squared the individual probabilities. This implies statistical *independence*. So, I conclude that you know *exactly* the cause of cot deaths?"

"Young man," he protested. "I never ever said such a thing!"

Mr Scott was on his feet again. "May I suggest to the judge that we stop this charade? It is evident that Mr Fielding has not followed one iota of Professor Goodwin's previous testimony!"

"Mr Fielding," said the judge, "if you are going to deform the testimony of the witness, I do indeed suggest we stop now."

"Please let me continue, my Lord. I will show how Professor Goodwin has indeed contradicted himself."

Judge Braithwaite looked around the court room. Suddenly he arched his eyebrows. He added wearily, "OK just a few more questions, but please be careful, Mr Fielding."

I decided to rewind a bit for clarity. "Professor, for double *murders* you say the events are statistically *dependant*. Once the first has happened, it is much more likely that the second will happen, because the first event proves the person has a higher risk of doing it again?"

"Yes, that is exactly what I said."

"But you say we do not know the cause of S.I.D.S.?"

"No, we do not."

I turned to the judge. "My Lord, we will now go through the arguments that if we do not know the cause of S.I.D.S., then it is *incorrect* to assume statistical *independence* such as Professor Goodwin has done by squaring the individual probabilities."

"I'm not sure I follow you," growled the judge. "But get on with it."

"Professor Goodwin," I said, "when you calculated your probability, you multiplied one in 8,500 by one in 8,500. You used exactly the same probability for the second cot death as you did for the first cot death. Why?"

"We do this because cot deaths appear randomly in the population." He now turned to the judge. "My Lord, contrary to Mr Fielding's assertions, when events are random, there is indeed statistical independence, and so the correct calculation is to square the individual probability. If you roll a dice and you randomly get a six, when you roll it again there is no more chance of having a six than of having any other number. It's random both times. In this simple example the chance of two sixes in a row is one out of six squared, that is one chance out of 36. About the same probability as juror number six being right twice in a row!" There was a chuckle around the courtroom at this jibe at my expense.

"Now, now, Professor, that will do," said the judge. "I'll give you my indulgence, seeing as you have yourself been the victim of the same from our rather too enthusiastic young juror here. Mr Fielding, even I can understand that the chances of two sixes in a row is one in six squared. Does that answer now satisfy you?"

"Not really, sir. Professor, you are specifically saying that if you have one cot death in the family, that doesn't create any more probability of having a second cot death in the same family?"

"That is exactly what I am saying."

"And you say this because a cot death is totally random.

94

It's like playing Russian roulette with a gun with 8,500 chambers, and only one of the chambers has a bullet in it? Each time you pull the trigger you have a one in 8,500 chance of a death."

"Yes, that explains it very well."

"Are there no external factors that contributed to the first cot death that then contribute to the second cot death?"

"No, I repeat, the data suggests it is purely random."

I'm glad you insist on that, I thought. I looked down at my notes. Yes, time to trip him up with a new argument. "But you said the one in 8,500 were the statistics for non-smoking families? Why did you use those statistics in particular?"

"Because the Richardsons are non-smokers. I wanted to be as close as possible to the true family environment," he answered.

"So, smoking increases the chances of S.I.D.S.?"

"Yes."

"I'm sorry," I said without feeling it in the least, "but in that case, you are contradicting yourself. It can't be completely random if smoking increases the odds."

"If you walk through a minefield, just like you are doing right now young man," bridled Goodwin, "everyone knows that you have a higher chance of being killed. Please don't play the naive fool with me; we all know that smoking is a serious health risk."

"But when was smoking finally recognised as being dangerous?"

"Right back in the 1950s, if I remember correctly."

"But smoking came to Europe from South America in the 1500s," I pointed out. "For four centuries nobody knew it was dangerous. Is it possible that, say, in 1900 – not so long ago really – after a heavy smoker has died of lung cancer, some eminent medical professor might have said, 'He died of some random arbitrary disease called cancer'?"

"Yes, I suppose so. But what are you trying to get at?" Goodwin sounded righteously irritated. "I told you I used the statistics of non-smoking families."

"My point is twofold. First, you assume that there are *only* random causes for S.I.D.S. Then you contradict yourself by saying smoking is a contributary cause."

"Which we agree seems pretty obvious."

"And I argue that for many centuries people were smoking in Europe without knowing it caused any problems. Only relatively recently has smoking been identified as a cause of lung cancer. Until then the causes of cancer appeared random, because people hadn't yet identified any of the causes.

"Now for S.I.D.S.," I continued, "you yourself admit that parents' smoking contributes – that is one cause you have so far identified. But then you say all the other reasons for S.I.D.S. are totally random. I disagree. It is simply that you *haven't yet identified* the other causes, so they *appear* random. In statistics when you see a *result* that appears random because you do not know the causes, you should not make the mistake of then assuming that the *causes* are also random. The causes, once known, are probably anything but random."

Goodwin chose not to react to this analysis.

I glanced down at my notes. "I would like to pursue another angle to the same idea. Have you ever had malaria?"

"No."

"What transmits it?"

"A bite from a mosquito that has previously bitten a malaria carrier," replied our medical expert, sounding puzzled by my question.

"Why is it called 'malaria'?"

"I'm not sure I know."

"That's a bit disingenuous, Professor Goodwin," I scolded kindly. "'Mal' means 'bad', 'aria' means 'air'. 'Bad air'. Did they not call the disease malaria because they originally thought that 'bad air' was infecting people?"

"Yes, I think you're right."

"So," I asked, "they had a completely wrong hypothesis – bad air – simply because they did not know?"

"Yes."

"Did everybody who got bitten by a mosquito catch malaria?"

"No, of course not. As I said, the mosquito had to have previously bitten a malaria carrier."

"So, there were two *combined* reasons." I counted them off with my thumb and forefinger. "One, to be bitten by a mosquito; two, that the mosquito had to have previously bitten a carrier?"

"Yes."

"Two variables combined. We know now. But we didn't know a couple of centuries back, did we? Each variable is *necessary* but on its own *not sufficient*. Yes?"

"Yes," confirmed Goodwin rather wearily, as if to suggest to everybody that I was going off at a tangent.

"Well," I countered, "I argue the same for S.I.D.S. Many variables could contribute. You already know one: smoking. But then, not all smokers' children die of S.I.D.S., do they?"

"No."

"It increases the risk but is not *alone* the cause. And indeed, non-smoker families can also be afflicted by S.I.D.S.; less than smokers' families, but afflicted nonetheless?"

"Yes." Again, the affected weariness in his voice.

"So, I repeat what I said before, just because we do not know the causes does not mean that there are no causes. It simply means we don't know. Therefore, it's not random, it's due to these causes – that we don't know – that makes it *appear* random. Do you agree?"

Goodwin decided to deflect the question. "I don't know what you are trying to get at. The result is clearly random."

"I strongly disagree," I insisted. "You are mixing up *appearing* to be random and *really* being random. If the causes are *not* random, the *same* causes would quite likely exist a second time around. They could be environmental, they could be genetic, and there are probably several causes, each one contributing to trigger this unlikely event. But if the first baby dies of cot death, quite probably this unlikely combination of causes is *also present* for the second baby. That means that the risk of the second baby dying as well is much higher. Thus, there *isn't* statistical *independence*, we have the opposite: statistical *dependence*."

I decided to plough on. "And if there are several causes that must be combined to trigger the event, it is almost impossible to test for them. There are too many, and each one individually doesn't give us the result. It's only when they happen together that tragedy strikes. So, since you can't test for them, you don't know them, so the result *appears* random.

"Let's take your example of a dice," I said to Goodwin.

"Without anyone knowing, the side opposite the six – the number one – is weighted. Mrs Richardson rolls the dice for the first time. She gets a six. You said her getting a six the first time does not mean she has more chance of getting a six the second time, because each roll of a dice is statistically independent. But you were assuming her dice is a normal random dice that is fair and not weighted.

"But," I continued, "if we then told you, 'by the way, her dice is weighted', you would immediately conclude, the weighting seems to favour the six, therefore there is more chance of her getting a six the second time. Suddenly, with this information, the rolling of the dice becomes statistically *dependent* – dependent on the result of the first roll."

I noticed the judge was slowly nodding his head in understanding. That was good news, I thought. Maybe he gambles with dice in his spare time.

Chapter Ten

"Let's come back to your data on S.I.D.S.," I said, looking at Goodwin. "On average you say only one out of 8,500 affluent, non-smoking families with older mothers suffer this tragedy. On average, right?"

"Yes," he replied.

"Professor, you remember what we said earlier: an average is made up of a collection of higher probabilities than one in 8,500 for some families, and lower probabilities for other families.

"Now without our originally knowing it," I went on, "the Richardson's dice is weighted due to environmental or genetic reasons, or quite possibly both. Mrs Richardson rolls the dice. Tragedy strikes, she loses her first baby. Given this information, we can imagine that there is a higher than one in 8,500 chance of tragedy striking a second time. Quite possibly a lot higher."

"Sorry, I beg to differ," argued Goodwin. "First, the police supplied my team with a full check on what they found in the environment in the Richardsons' home. Our analysis found no reason to suppose that this was contributing to the deaths. Secondly, there is clear evidence of no genetic history of infant deaths in either families. To use your very own logic of a weighted dice, this means there would be even *less* chance of S.I.D.S. happening in their case than on average, not more!"

I shook my head in wonder at what he had just said, and it was the second time he had used the 'clear evidence' term in two days. He must have rehearsed it. Now I was going to have some fun...

"You checked the environment and found no reason that this was the origin of the deaths?" I asked. "How on earth can you check when you don't know what to look for? Apart from smoking that is. Could it not be something in the mattress? Some residue from a hidden insect in the woodwork? The father's after-shave lotion? Since you don't know, it could be just about anything."

I went in for the kill. "Then you say, 'there is clear evidence of no genetic history of infant deaths'? Is this perjury or are you just incompetent?!"

"Mr Fielding," roared the judge, "you will abstain from any such insinuations or insults in this court. I've half a mind to hold you in contempt!"

"My Lord, if you give me time, I can demonstrate that this extraordinary statement has to be untrue, so that it is either one or the other!"

The judge, furious, glanced to his left. Shaking his head, he seemed to count to three to calm down. "Get on with it then!" he barked.

"Professor Goodwin," I said, "you are a man of medicine.

If I had had cancer, and seemed to be in remission, you would take blood samples to see if I had any cancerous cells still around?"

"Yes."

"And if you found none, what would you conclude?"

"That you have been cured."

"Might you conclude, if I may paraphrase your words, that there was 'clear evidence of no disease'?"

"Yes," said Goodwin.

"Did you test all my cells, or only a small sample?"

"We can only test a sample. It would kill the patient to test every last one of his cells!"

"So, the cancer cells could still be hiding somewhere that you did not test?" I asked.

"Er, yes conceivably."

"However, you just said 'clear evidence of no disease'. How can you be so sure? How do you prove a negative? Actually, it's impossible to prove a negative. Would you not have to test every single last cell of my body in order to prove a negative?"

"Er…" hesitated Goodwin. "No, we can't be 100% sure, but statistically there is a very good chance that it's gone."

"May I dare to say that you are mixing up two fundamentally different statistical notions: 'evidence of no disease' is *not* the same thing as 'no evidence of disease'?"

"I see your point," he conceded. "Well; yes, strictly you should say 'no evidence of disease'."

"Now," I said, "may we come back to the genetics survey you did of the defendant's family? I argue you cannot say 'clear evidence of no genetic history of infant deaths', you can only say 'you found no evidence of genetic history of S.I.D.S.'. Do you agree?"

"Yes, put that way I suppose I have to agree. But it really is splitting hairs…"

"Splitting hairs?" I said indignantly. "Can you convict someone simply because you found no evidence that can prove their probable innocence? Does not the burden of proof come to the prosecution?"

"I repeat, we did a thorough search of family history," said Goodwin defensively.

"I am a little curious as to your conclusions from this research." I glanced at my notes. "If some distant family siblings or cousins died in infancy, they are not around to talk about it, are they? Had you considered the bias in your research of what is called 'silent evidence' – the evidence to prove the contrary to your hypothesis is no longer there because this same evidence died off?"

"I repeat we did significant research. Through questionnaires to branches of the family and going through church records."

"Asking who? Did all the families boast about, or even know about, infant deaths of siblings, cousins or great aunts? Is there a church record if an infant died before it was christened some 100 years ago? Can you really be sure of your data?"

"I am satisfied with our research," he insisted.

"And how far did you go back?" I asked. "For arguments sake, let's say this is a gene that increases the probability of a cot death by 100-to-1,000 times the average, which means we would expect between one death in 85 births to one death in 8.5 births – still fortunately a relatively rare event. Might you not have to go back at least ten or more generations to find it at work?"

I turned to the judge. "May I have a calculator, please, or a calculator app on a smartphone?" One of the ushers pulled out his phone, he glanced at the judge who nodded his assent, then he opened his calculator app and passed the phone to me. I quickly calculated two to the power of ten, "That's over 1,000 great, great… I don't know how many great, grandparents to check out over the last 300 years? Did you do all that?"

"No that would have been impossible," said Goodwin.

"How many relatives did you check out?"

"About twenty."

"Going back how many generations?" I asked.

"Two or three."

"So, you checked out only two per cent of my proposed list of over 1,000 possible ancestors and went back only a quarter of the period in time? Was your sample size statistically large enough, Professor? Remember, we are only looking for one rare event, not for a series. I ask you again, could this rare gene conceivably be in the defendant's, or the defendant's husband's, genetic make-up?"

"Conceivably yes, but I still count it very unlikely," conceded Goodwin.

"And finally, could it be the presence of two different genes that trigger S.I.D.S.? Both are necessary, but neither one alone is sufficient – like in our malaria example. Can we exclude this?"

"No, I suppose we cannot exclude this."

"What if one gene came from the mother's side, and the other gene came from the father's side? I ask you, even if you did an exhaustive check of a hundred per cent of all the ancestors, would any cot deaths show up if these two genes have not yet met?"

"Er, no, in that scenario they would not show up any cot deaths," said Goodwin.

"So," I said, "in conclusion, you cannot exclude the possibility of cot deaths being due to genes, and you cannot exclude the possibility of such genes being in the deceased children. Am I right?"

"I repeat," said Goodwin, "I have seen plenty of evidence that child abuse goes from one generation to the next, but none to suggest that S.I.D.S. does. However, I also accept that we cannot completely exclude this."

"In the light of this discussion, let's do a thought experiment." I said. "Assume a case where there is a genetic predisposition to S.I.D.S., but we don't know which gene. Although the average data from the population would give us an apparent statistical randomness, in reality a family having this gene would have an increased probability of having a baby that dies of S.I.D.S., when compared to the average probability. Correct?"

"This is your thought experiment, not mine."

"Professor Goodwin," interceded the judge, "please answer the question. Mr Fielding, please repeat."

"Is there an increased chance of one family with this gene having S.I.D.S.?" I asked.

"Yes, in *your* thought experiment," said Goodwin.

"If the gene increased the probability of S.I.D.S. by a factor of, say, 100, what would be the likely probability of one death?"

"Er, for the Richardson's household that would be

one in 8,500 divided by one hundred, which makes one in 85."

"What then would be the probability for a family having this gene suffering two deaths?"

"85 times 85." Goodwin used his phone and calculated. "One chance in 7,200."

"One chance in 7,200? Is that not 10,000 times smaller than your previously calculated one chance in 72 million?" I asked.

"Yes," he said.

"And if by mischance, the genetic risk multiplied the original probability by as much as 1,000, the probability of two deaths would reduce to one in only 8.5 multiplied by 8.5," this time I did the calculation on the usher's phone, "so one in only 72?"

"Don't push your luck."

"Professor Goodwin, please answer the question!" ordered the judge.

"Yes, in the extremely unlikely case that the genes multiplied the probability by a thousand, it would be one in 72."

"We really are very far from your stipulation of one in 72 million," I said.

I carried on. "If there are approximately 800,000 births a year in the UK, and if we continue to use the very high one in 8,500 that you insist applies to the Richrdsons, then we can expect..." I typed in the figures on the phone's calculator, "about 94 cot deaths a year. OK so far?"

"As we saw earlier, in reality there would be more

nationwide, including those families who are smokers, unemployed or have young mothers" said Goodwin.

"OK, let's remain very conservative," I said. "Let's assume that a bit more than half of these parents try again – they want a baby, and they will want to forget the death as soon as possible. So, each year there's around 50 parents having suffered one cot death now trying for another baby. If the cause is genetic, then probably these 50 parents have this gene. Let's take our lower bound of a one in 85 chance of having another cot death… 50 divided by 85," I typed in the figures, "gives 0.6 of these babies as dying, already more than one case of double cot death in the UK every two years! If we take the upper bound of one in 8.5 dying, then there are ten times more, that's six double cot deaths per year! Do you agree with the maths?"

"OK, but only assuming that you multiply the odds by 100 to 1,000 due to a strong genetic influence. Your assumptions, not mine," said Goodwin.

"Now," I said, "we agreed at the beginning: the accused is not some random person we found on the streets. She is here precisely because she has suffered two cot deaths. According to these corrected statistics, there will be say between one person every two years at least, and six people a year at most, in the UK, in her position of suffering two cot deaths."

There was a hushed silence in the courtroom. Even the prosecution barrister was silently shaking his head in dismay.

"Professor Goodwin, do you agree with these calculations?" I asked.

"Only if the cause were genetic," he said, "and if your probability assumptions were correct, both of which I doubt."

"Can you *prove* to me that my assumptions are wrong?"

"Er, no."

"And we saw a similar argument if the cause is environmental, didn't we?"

"Yes, we did."

"And in each case, it's the same genes and the same environment, isn't it?"

"Yes." Goodwin sounded deflated.

"So, Professor, now is your chance to redeem yourself," I said. "We had what appeared to be one of two unlikely events – either double natural death or double murder. It now seems that two natural deaths have a higher probability of occurring then we first thought. In your expert opinion, is the probability of the defendant's children dying of natural deaths greater or lesser than the probability of her intentionally killing them both?"

"I'm sorry, but we cannot rule out the marks on the second baby's face that suggests evidence of smothering. That changes the calculation. There is suspicion of foul play, even if you argue those marks alone could not prove murder. We are no longer talking about your famous 4 million different 'attempts' at double cot deaths. Those marks are there only on Mrs Richardson's baby, not on the other 3,999,999 other births. Only her baby. That makes her a suspect. And *once* she is suspect, she *then* only has a one in 72 million chance with my statistics, or a one in 72 chance even with your most optimistic gene altered statistics, of being innocent." Godwin glared at me in his intellectual triumph.

I must confess, this stymied me. My mind whirled on what had he just said. Had I underestimated the probabilistic impact of these marks? Was what he said right? I decided, perhaps rather foolhardily, to reason out loud, because my gut feel told me that what he had just said did not add up. "I understand what you are saying, but intuitively it doesn't make sense. Let me explain my reasoning. Assume that what you call my most optimistic gene altered statistics are correct. We get six or more babies dying each year following two subsequent cot deaths. I would say that there is a good chance that either the mother, father or ambulance crew, someone will try to resuscitate these babies, each time. Our pathologist admitted that resuscitation might well be the cause of the marks. So, at least some out of those six babies might have those marks. Are we going to throw each of those families into jail for murder?"

Suddenly I realised that I had just stated the right answer. "That's it, of course!" I exclaimed. "Contrary to what you say, those marks are *not specific* to Mrs Richardson's case. They are to be expected *each* time we get a cot death. This means that any parent who suffers the same bad luck has a good chance of also being accused of being a murder suspect, because there is a good chance of there being these same marks on the baby's face. Your reasoning would have been correct if, and only if, those marks would be truly specific to Mrs Richardson's case."

Goodwin looked non-plussed but did not say anything.

"Do you agree, Professor?" I asked. "Are those marks uniquely specific to Mrs Richardson, or do you not admit that we might see them in any cot death case?"

"It's possible," he finally admitted. "But I still think unlikely." He was not going to back down easily.

"But again," I asked, "can you *prove* to the court that we will *not* get these marks each time there is a cot death?"

"No, I can't prove it," he conceded.

"So, I ask you again," I said, "with these revised figures, in your expert opinion, is the probability of the accused's children dying of natural causes greater or lesser than the probability of her intentionally killing them both?"

"Only if your assumptions on the gene effect were correct," replied Goodwin, "which I repeat I don't believe, only in that case would we have the possibility of a higher probability of deaths from natural causes."

"But do you confirm that you cannot prove that my assumptions are wrong? For example, you cannot prove that there is not a gene that increases the probability of S.I.D.S.?"

"No. I don't believe it, but I cannot prove it."

"Therefore, by extension, you *cannot prove* statistically that these deaths were murder?" I asked.

There was silence for two seconds. "No," he finally said.

"So, do you retract your initial testimony that you can *prove* that the cause of death was intentional killing?"

Again, silence for a few seconds. "I maintain my conviction that this was murder. But I need to revisit my statistical analysis to counter your arguments. So today, no, I do not have the proof that the court needs," said Goodwin.

The judge looked to the far-left rear of the court with a small smile on his face, nodding slightly. Then he turned to me. "Thank you, Mr Fielding. Nicely done. Does the prosecution wish to re-examine this witness? I personally would advise caution given the fact that he has formally retracted his proof."

Scott had a heated discussion with his junior and with the solicitor from the Crown Prosecution Team.

"No, my Lord," he said. "And as this was our last witness, I will close by saying that this is the case for the Crown."

The judge turned towards the witness stand. "Professor Goodwin, you are free to go." He then turned to the defence. "Mr Dawkins, in light of this, how do you wish to proceed?"

Dawkins discussed with his team, then he stood up. "Given the empty state of the prosecution's case, we prefer to stop here and say that this is also the case for the defence. I should thus like to make an application to you, my Lord."

"I understand," said the judge nodding. "We shall now break for lunch. I wish to meet with counsel at 2pm. Jury keepers, please keep the jury ready in their room until I call you."

We all stood as the judge marched out. Then our keepers promptly led us out of the courtroom.

Chapter Eleven

Once back in our jury room, this time there was some backslapping and forthcoming comments of congratulations.

Even business suit (David was his name) spontaneously said, "I thought at one point that you were all over the place, but the way you finally brought it all together was just excellent. Bravo!"

One of the previous evening's detractors was (slightly) less aggressive. "Still didn't understand a bloody word you said; but it must have been good otherwise his nibs wouldn't have backed down, would he?"

But Mrs die-hard (Beth, actually) was not to be detracted. "What 'ave you gone and done? This woman's suffering from that F.D... wotsits disease, she shook the life out of 'er first child, they found smovering marks on 'er poor second baby's mouth, that's good enough for me. She's killed twice, so we'd better stop trying to find excuses for 'er, before she kills again. You and all your big words and your big ideas. You confused the professor, you confused the judge, and you confused me! You even forced that poor man to say black when 'e was saying white."

David came to my help. "Calm down, Beth. You're entitled to your opinion; but in a court of law opinion won't do. You have to be convinced beyond any reasonable doubt. Young Martin here has shown there's so much doubt in this case that you can drive a double decker bus through it. Personally, I'm now convinced it's natural causes. When my wife got pregnant the first time, she had a miscarriage. For her next pregnancy, she spent three months lying in bed. Why? Because the doctor told her that if she has already had a first miscarriage, then there is a high risk of her having a second. Well, why can't it be the same thing for cot deaths? Can you imagine a poor mother that has lost two babies for tragic natural reasons, then being put into prison for murder despite being innocent? How terrible that would be?"

It seemed that most people agreed with David.

Hilary, our foreperson, decided to intervene. "Look, everybody, this isn't yet the time for jury deliberation. I suggest we eat our lunch and wait for our next instructions from the judge, OK?"

Hunger pangs decided that this was a good proposal, so we attacked the day's offering. There were ample portions of quiche Lorraine (I remember my dad quoting the title of a book called *Real Men Don't Eat Quiche*, which apparently split the world into doers and poseurs; to which my mum countered that 'real men eat quiche and don't read that book'.) There was also some limp lettuce, Heinz salad dressing, a modest cheese board and some French baguettes (or rather English bread shaped into long loaves imitating the shapes of baguettes).

"If you don't eat the bread, then this is almost your Montignac diet," joked Stephanie.

"More like food for the real food," I countered.

"By the way, well done again. As the French would say, it was certainly gale force and coming in far above our heads!"

"That's anatomically impossible."

While we were all waiting and drinking our second cups of weak coffee out of not very ecological plastic cups, served from the rather tired thermos, the judge was talking to counsel. This is what I later gleaned of the discussion from my same sources.

"Mr Dawkins," asked the judge, "you wished to make an application to me?"

"Yes, my Lord. I wish to make a half time submission of no case to answer. There is either no evidence left in the prosecution's case, or whatever remaining evidence there is, it's insufficient to support a conviction."

"Mr Scott?"

"The prosecution has rested its case, my Lord. I have nothing more to say. This is your decision."

"This is a trial for murder, Mr Dawkins," said the judge. "As such, before I can decide on your application, I require you to reconfirm to me that the defence does not wish to present any witnesses, and that you also rest your case?"

"I confirm, my Lord."

"Very well, in that case I fully agree to this submission." The judge turned to the court clerk. "Please bring in the jury."

"Members of the jury," said the judge solemnly, "the defence has made an application called a 'submission of no case to answer'. The prosecution has not opposed this application. Furthermore, the defence has reconfirmed that they also rest their case.

"So, under the Criminal Procedure Rules Part 25.9 brackets 2, paragraph (e), I have decided to direct you, the jury, to acquit the defendant on the grounds that the prosecution's evidence is insufficient for any reasonable court to convict.

"I do this because after this morning's retraction by the expert witness, the prosecution's case is weak, with virtually no evidence left, and what is left is certainly insufficient to convict. I would go further; we have seen that a more rigorous analysis of the information fully exonerates the defendant of any crime.

"For the sake of clarity, and to clear up any doubt in the jury, or indeed in the public at large," here the judge cast his eye over the journalists on the public benches, "I wish to go through rapidly all the accusations we originally heard from the prosecution, and to give you a summary of the evidence and arguments you have heard that refute this."

The judge glanced down at his notes. "First, the suspicious marks around the baby's mouth. The pathologist himself admitted to the court that he did not believe at the time that this was anything other than a natural death, and he agreed that they could have been due to the resuscitation effort. Concerning the retrospective speculation that the first child Andrew might have been shaken, although the defence chose to rest their case before bringing in an eye expert to formally contest this, the prosecution's own paediatric expert, who agreed he is not an eye specialist, confirmed there was an open disagreement between himself and the more qualified expert on this issue. In any case, this previous death is formally not part of this court's remit.

"Next, the order of the telephone calls. The police officer handling the investigation confirmed to the court that a person trained in advanced first aid should be able to determine when someone has died. This lightens markedly the question mark as to why the defendant did not call an ambulance before calling her husband.

"Next, the diagnosis of F.D.I.A., that is, a syndrome where a mother might deliberately harm one of her children. We only have one expert's diagnosis, without ever having interviewed the patient. We do not have any second opinion. Together this renders the diagnosis at best insufficient, at worse suspect.

"Furthermore, the defence has pointed out that many of the preceding suspicions may be an attempt to fit a narrative *ex-post* to support a theory of murder, a theory originally suggested by a dubious analysis of statistics, rather than there being clear evidence on its own. The defence suggested there was a circular argument – F.D.I.A. syndrome is one of the only credible reasons for the mother to commit murder if the statistics are to be believed; and once you believe in the F.D.I.A. diagnosis, it makes the apparent statistical analysis all the more credible. Then the rather loose medical arguments seem to be forcibly retrofitted to support all this, even going against other medical experts' opinions. With a circular argument, once you break it, in this case the statistics seem manifestly to be wrong, then all the other arguments fail.

"Finally, for the statistical evidence, this depended on only one expert witness, and he formally retracted himself this morning. Thanks to Mr Fielding's intervention, we detect several flaws in his original argument:

"There are millions of births happening. The sheer number of events allows even very unlikely 'bad-luck' events to eventually happen, just like the 'good-luck' counter example, one out of the 50 million people who buys a lottery ticket will win the lottery.

"Our expert made a mistake in assuming that the average for a population applied to each individual in that population. His own statistics showed us incredible variations were possible, some conditions gave forty times more likelihood of a cot death than others. He used the worst possible combination, and squared it to get his one in 72 million. Even using his own flawed logic, if we square the probability that is forty times larger, I calculate we get down to odds of one in only 45,000, not much considering the millions of births. I understand this error made by our expert witness is called the 'ecological fallacy'.

"Our expert witness did not compare the probabilities of two hypotheses of rare events – cot death and murder, once the rare event of double deaths had already happened. He only analysed the stand-alone probability of double cot deaths, which was also a mistake. I am given to understand this is called the 'prosecutor's fallacy'.

"We have now understood that random results do not mean random causes, therefore the cause of cot deaths may not be random.

"As such there may be triggers due to the environment and/or due to genes. Our expert witness eventually confirmed that he did not do anywhere near enough searches to eliminate genes as a cause.

"Hence, we may well have statistical dependence rather than statistical independence, which would be the equivalent of having a weighted dice. In which case, you cannot simply square the stand-alone probability: since the first cot death could indicate a dramatic increase in probability for a second cot death.

"Given these possibilities, Mr Fielding came up with a credible scenario where you could find anything between one cot death in the UK every two years, right up to six cot deaths every year. The possibility of this scenario was confirmed, even if unwillingly, by the expert.

"And Mr Fielding points out that Mrs Richardson is in court precisely because she is one of the unlucky ones to whom this tragedy has happened.

"That is why, ladies and gentlemen of the jury, I direct you to find a verdict of not guilty to exonerate the defendant.

"Finally, we need a unanimous verdict. Please put any thoughts of a majority verdict out of your minds unless I give you further instructions."

Way to go, judge! I thought. You must have suddenly remembered your O-level in maths. That was just an incredible summary!

We went off to the jury room. The jury keeper stood right outside the door. He obviously did not expect us to take long. Hilary had us all sit down.

"We have been directed to find a verdict of not guilty. Is there any reason to disagree?" she asked.

Most people were shaking their heads. Even Beth said nothing; she just looked down at the table.

"Hands up for not guilty, then," said Hilary. All hands

went up – those of us twelve official jurors, as well as those of the two substitutes just for good measure. "So, we return a unanimous verdict of not guilty."

"Looks like we'll be going home earlier than expected," said David. "Two days for a murder trial! Before we go back into the courtroom, I'm curious to know how we would have voted if Martin hadn't destroyed Professor Goodwin's bad statistics. Personally, it's only after listening to Martin that I made the parallel with my wife's miscarriages: that cot deaths are probably statistically dependent and not independent. At the time, although I thought the medical proof was a bit iffy, I was blinded by that one in 72 million statistic. I was sure at that point she was guilty. Be honest, what did you others think?"

Different people round the table nodded their agreement, and added their comments: "I agree," said one.

"No way did I think it could it be an accidental death with a one to 72 million chance against it," said another.

"That was exactly my reasoning too," said a third.

"Me too, she was guilty as sin until Martin waded in," said a fourth.

"God forgive me, I thought she was guilty too," another said.

"Me too," yet another said; and so on.

"Let's have an unofficial straw poll just for curiosity," said David. "When the defence sat down, just before Martin gave his list of questions to the judge, who had already decided she was guilty? Hands up!"

Thirteen hands went slowly and somewhat embarrassingly up, including the two substitutes.

"You too, Stephanie?" I asked.

119

"Yes, sorry, at first I thought she was guilty," she replied. "Professor Sir Michael Goodwin is so well known. He's got more initials after his name then there are letters in the alphabet. And in my line of business when a medical professor speaks, his word is gospel. And how can you not vote guilty if you are told the odds of natural deaths are 72 million to one?! Even if you just can't believe a mother would do that to her children."

"Eleven to one would have led to a majority vote of guilty," said David. "That poor lady would have spent most of the rest of her life in prison. Not only did she have the tragedy of losing her two sons, each of us would have contributed to the second tragedy of wrongfully convicting her. We have so narrowly escaped a travesty of justice. Thanks, Martin, for not letting us do that! What luck the judge let you cross-examine that professor."

"Even if I hadn't been allowed to cross-examine," I said, "I wouldn't have let you leave this jury room until I had convinced each one of you of Goodwin's manifest errors."

"Manifest to you, perhaps," said David, "but not to us. It would have been *Twelve Angry Men* all over again!"

"Twelve Angry Men and Women!" added Hilary. "I hope you would have succeeded Martin. Thank you for stopping me sending an innocent woman to prison. Now let's just hope she can begin to piece her life back together after all that has happened to her."

"For those who did at least some maths at school," I said, "I would have hassled you with Bayes' theorem derived from simple first principles. This shows that the probability of two cot deaths is irrelevant; the only statistic that counts is the ratio of the probability of double murder to that of double cot deaths. That's the crux of the prosecutor's fallacy. Even you would have understood it, David!"

"Thanks, Martin," he replied sarcastically, but with a chortle.

"Hang on," I added in my enthusiasm, "I worked out the Bayes' equation for this situation late last night."

I went to the flip chart and wrote:

$$P(2CD \mid 2D) = 1 \,/\, [\, 1 + P(2M)/P(2CD)\,]^{1}$$

"On the left is the probability of two cot deaths (2CD) having happened, given that the rare event of two deaths (2D) *has already happened*," I explained to mostly very puzzled faces, some of which were totally aghast. "That basically means the probability of her being innocent. On the right we see that it is a function of... er, that means depends on, the *ratio* of $P(2M)$ – which is the probability of two murders having happened – divided by $P(2CD)$ – which is the probability of two cot deaths having happened. Both $P(2M)$ and $P(2CD)$ are incredibly small numbers. But if a double murder is, say, ten times less likely than a double cot death, not unexpectedly this equation gives the chances of her being innocent at about 90% (91% to be exact). At no point in time is her chance of being innocent just simply equal to $P(2CD)$ – the very small stand-alone probability of two cot deaths *before* any deaths have actually happened, as Professor Goodwin tried to make us believe. In fact, the one to 72 million is a totally irrelevant statistic!"

---

1   See the appendix for the derivation of Bayes' theorem from first principals, and then the 'Bayesian flip' to get this equation.

"You talking bloody double-dutch again, you is," said Beth.

"That's enough, Martin," said Hilary, who probably agreed with Beth. "We've got a judge and courtroom waiting for us."

"If," said David as he stood up, "you could have convinced me how you derived that equation, Martin, and that you hadn't just invented it out of thin air, maybe I would have followed your reasoning, and perhaps one or two others here would have as well, and perhaps together we could have convinced enough of the others to acquit. *Maybe*. But if you *hadn't* been on this jury," he added, "it's almost sure we would have found her guilty..."

On that sober note, Hilary summoned the jury keeper and we all tramped back into the courtroom.

Back in court, the judge asked our foreperson if we had reached a unanimous verdict on the count of murder of George Richardson.

"Yes, my Lord," replied Hilary.

"And what is it?"

"Not guilty." There was an audible sigh of relief around the courtroom.

The judge turned to the defendant. "Mrs Richardson, you are free to go."

She was sobbing uncontrollably, but she nodded her thanks. Poor woman, I thought, to have lost two sons and then have to put up with the accusation that she had killed them.

Back in the public benches I saw what I assumed to be her husband, and her family, all hugging each other in relief after their months of ordeal.

Some journalists were already beginning to stand up to get out and make their reports. Others were already hard at work thumbing away on their smartphones without moving places.

The judge addressed the court. "Before we end this trial, I would just like to add a couple of comments." Any people standing up then gingerly sat down again. The judge turned to the public benches where our esteemed professor was now sitting meekly since the lunch break.

"Professor Goodwin, you are a renowned paediatrician, and yet you seem to have ignored some basic scientific principals in your testimony, that even a young engineer, who we are fortunate to have with us today, was able to unwind quite rapidly. I would not go so far as to say that you have committed perjury, but your lack of rigour does in my opinion disqualify you from ever giving testimony in court again. Please take note. Personally, I think you are a disgrace to your honourable profession.

"I am given to understand that your expert testimony has already been used to convict in several other cases of infant mortality. I have no other recourse than to formally request to the Lord Chief Justice that all these cases are reopened and re-evaluated in the light of your statistical and professional mistakes disclosed today.

"Ladies and gentlemen of the jury. You are dismissed and are excused further jury duties."

Chapter Twelve

As we were gathering our phones and other items from our lockers, Beth could be heard complaining. "I was 'oping for the £130 daily allowance you get for a long trial, that's more than I get at work. It's only £65 a day for short trials, multiplied by two flipping days, that's nuffin'. And all thanks to this guy," she added cocking her head at me while going off in a huff.

Stephanie and I laughed, but not for long. "Some innocent mother almost got a life sentence, and all she can think about is her indemnities!" said Stephanie.

"Since our time together as jurors has been dramatically cut short by some young fool," I said, "may I now dare invite you out to dinner later this evening? Or would that cause some boyfriend to be too jealous?" My oh my, I thought, wasn't I getting a little too bold and a little too direct?

"Well," she said, "there's nobody currently qualified to be jealous, although a few boring doctors would like to think otherwise." (That sounded hopeful!) "But I will only accept on condition you let me eat chips with my steak!"

"Deal!" I laughed.

We agreed on a time, and I said I would send her an SMS with the restaurant's details once I had found a suitable reservation. We kissed each other goodbye on both cheeks, but I was convinced our mouths were a bit closer than they were supposed to be.

On the way out through the main entrance hall, I bumped into a face that I vaguely knew. Wasn't it the person who had been sitting in the far-left rear of the courtroom? Yes, but hadn't I seen that face before somewhere else? He looked a bit like a nightclub bouncer, or maybe an enforcer for some East-end gang. He came over to congratulate me. "Excellent job," he said, in an American accent. (Not East End then, I thought, maybe New York mafia? Has he been hired by the prosecution to beat me up?) "I suspect you've been reading some of my books. My name's Nassim Taleb."

My jaw dropped. *The* Nassim Taleb? The guy who wrote *Fooled By Randomness*, and even more spectacular, *The Black Swan* on unexpected events. The guy who predicted the unlikely event of a financial crisis due to 'fat tails'? My favourite author! I had seen his photograph on the back of his books. In his third book, *Antifragile*, he explains that some systems actually get stronger thanks to stressors. He also explained that he likes to practice what he preaches, so to stress his body he works out with weights, and now nobody dares to argue with him.

"An honour to meet you, Mr Taleb!" I said shaking his hand. "And an even greater honour to be congratulated by you." Suddenly I clicked on the judge's wavering attitudes. "Were you signalling or something to the judge from the back of the court?"

"Yup!" he replied. "The judge knew he was out of his depth when he tried reading your questions. He also knew he had taken an enormous risk in getting you to ask the questions himself. Yesterday evening he asked around for a probability expert. One of his learned friends had read my books and had just attended a conference here in London last week where I was one of the speakers, on 'Uncertainty in the financial markets'.

"The judge managed to wrangle my mobile phone number from the conference organisers, probably threatened them with a life sentence or something, and he rang me last night. He was happy to hear that I was still in London. He explained the situation to me, read out your written questions and gave me a brief summary of your cross-examination so far. He then asked if he should hire you or fire you. Well, he didn't actually use that language. Far too polite."

"And what did you say?" I asked.

"I told him to hang on in there, that they had hit gold by having you in the courtroom," he replied. "I also suggested that he should throw the expert out on his ass, and that the defence lawyer should be debarred for incompetence in not having better prepared. I probably used slightly different wording as well. I don't often talk to Lords."

"He's not a Lord, although that's what they call him."

"You Brits! Why make it simple when you can make it complicated?"

"But thanks for the job reference. How come you were in court?"

"Well the judge made me a proposal," said Taleb. "He would take me out to the best restaurant in London if I would sit at the back of the court today and signal if you were on the ball or if you were bullshitting. Given the teasers he'd already explained to me, I told him I wouldn't miss the show for anything. So, I cancelled everything I'd planned to do today, and here I am.

"We'd decided together that my pen pointing in the air meant what you were saying was good; and if it pointed down than you were in deep water. I texted him a photo of me so he would recognise me in court. I can tell you; you did a really good job! Hardly ever did my pen point down. He was just about to fire you for talking about perjury when he saw me actively shaking my tip towards the ceiling. I knew you'd hit gold dust with that fool's description of 'evidence of no genetic precedent'. Did you get that from my book *The Black Swan*?"

"What me? An engineer? I don't know how to read!" Something else clicked. "You didn't give him any help with the summing up by any chance?" I asked.

"What? I'm sure that would be unethical," he said. "But I guess judges can phone whom they want in their meal breaks. So how come you knew all about Bayes' theorem and the prosecutor's fallacy?"

"We covered it in our probability maths," I answered. "To illustrate it we first looked at the probabilities of mammography testing for cancer. The test is judged to have a 90% accuracy rate; so people testing positive wrongly assumed they had a 90% chance of cancer. They didn't correctly account for the false positives. If I remember correctly, some 0.3% of women risk having breast cancer, so using Bayes' theorem you can quickly calculate that if a woman tests positive, she still only has a 3% risk of cancer. Which is logical anyway if you understand the notion of a false positive: the mammography eliminates nine out of ten women with no risk; so that if you are not eliminated by the test your risk goes up ten times from 0.3% to 3%. But just like in the prosecutor's fallacy, the real probability of cancer after a positive mammography, 3%, was often being confused with the 90% accuracy rate.

"Our lecturer then extended this concept to the courtrooms, where the prosecution might make the fallacy of assuming that the probability of a random match of evidence is equal to the probability that the defendant is guilty. In the pre-DNA days, if the police find a certain blood type at the scene of the crime that only 10% of the population have, and the defendant has this blood type, then the prosecution might say he has 90% chance of being guilty; whereas by using Bayes' theorem – and common sense! – if there are, say, 100 suspects and this guy was pulled out at random, the fact he has the same blood type means he has only a 10% chance of being guilty."

"You know there is also a similar, almost mirror image misuse of statistics called the defence attorney's fallacy?" asked Taleb.

"No, I didn't."

"It was used by the defence in the O.J. Simpson trial in 1994 for the murder of his ex-wife," he explained. "The prosecution underlined that there was previous proof of Simpson beating his wife, which could only increase the likelihood of his guilt already derived from other evidence. But the defence used statistics to show that only one out of 2,500 battered women went on to be killed by their battering spouse, therefore the prosecution's statements were irrelevant to the trial, and should be ignored. 'Effect given cause', the probability of the effect, being killed, due to the cause, a battering spouse, only one 2,500; 'so jury please ignore this' they said.

"But what the defence cleverly omitted from their calculation was 'cause given effect'," he continued. "Simpson's ex-wife had indeed been murdered; the 'effect' was already there, it wasn't hypothetical. And here the one out of 2,500 statistic was totally irrelevant. Again, using Bayes' theorem, what counted was, once you've got a dead body, what is the ratio of probability of being murdered by a spouse known to beat his wife, divided by the global probability of murder? The answer is a much higher one in 3.5. But that didn't come out in the trial. That, and some equally erroneous arguments from the defence on the DNA statistics led him to be acquitted."

"It would seem no statistics should ever be quoted in court without some mathematician to comment on their validity," I suggested.

"That would certainly be better than nothing," Taleb agreed, "but many so-called mathematicians also quite often get it totally wrong. Fat tails... need I say any more?"

"I take your point!" I laughed.

"There were mathematicians at this latest financial conference, here in London, falling into the same trap as before," he said. "Everyone was saying how sub-primes could never happen again; I just said the next financial crisis won't be sub-primes but some other vastly correlated event that nobody sees coming. I imagine you get the irony of the parallel between the trial you've just wound up and the 2008 financial crisis?"

"You mean our dear Professor Goodwin making the very same mistake as all those rating agencies giving AAA risk-free status to those toxic, sub-prime mortgage securities that caused the crisis?" I asked.

"Yup. Got it in one!"

I shook my head in wonder as I took in the enormity of the parallel. "He squared the individual probabilities of cot deaths," I said thinking out loud, "which assumes statistical independence: one cot death happening has no influence on the probability of another death, he is saying. Unbelievably, all the great banks in the world, and those rating agencies did the same thing before 2008. Because the mortgage securities were made up of loans to thousands and thousands of different houses, they assumed only one or two houses would lose money, but never all the houses at the same time. It can't happen, they said, just like Goodwin said there couldn't be two accidental deaths in a row. But just like the Professor, they assumed statistical *independence*, whereas in reality there was statistical *dependence*. How could they not see that when a property speculation bubble bursts, *all* those houses lose value at the *same* time? All those so-called risk-free securities suddenly all become toxic sub-prime mortgages."

"But they didn't see it," said Taleb. "They missed the correlation – when one mortgage takes a nose drive, there is every risk that the others are doing the same. Just like if one family has a cot death, there is every risk that a second could follow. And right here, did the defence counsel see Goodwin's evident mistakes? Or did the other members of your jury see it?"

"No, they didn't," I confirmed. "In both cases it's obvious when you think about it. But in both cases people are blind to the obvious with catastrophic consequences. That poor woman could have been sentenced to life in prison."

"Just like trillions of dollars of people's hard-earned pension funds were lost in the crisis," he said. "And just four days ago at that conference, some of the world's top financial wizards were saying it couldn't happen again because we learnt our lesson about mortgage securities. I couldn't believe my ears. It's almost irrelevant what underlying event caused the crisis, the whole point is that nearly *everything* is *correlated*, with knock-on effects that can cause things to happen everywhere, virtually at the same time. They are right to say the next crisis won't be due to sub-primes, but they are so *wrong* to say that there *won't be another crisis*. It could be anything next time, maybe some unheard-of virus mutating and infecting everybody around the world. Nobody could then say that someone falling ill in Delhi is statistically independent to someone else getting ill in New York! Just think what the stock markets would do if worldwide you couldn't go to work for fear of being infected!"

"Don't be such a pessimist!" I said. "I doubt that could happen. You'll be talking about nuclear annihilation next, with statistically correlated tweets between two egocentric presidents winding each other up, action and reaction, leading to first strike and counter-strike!"

"Better to have the virus," he said. "Then at least some of us might survive. The human race as a whole could be anti-fragile and survive a virus attack thanks to antibodies, but not to a nuclear attack. But anyway, before someone pushes the wrong button or some deadly virus mutates, it's me who'll take you out to dinner – but to the cheapest place I can find – and we'll talk about some research projects that I've got coming up in the USA that might interest you! Are you free tonight?"

"Ah, no. I've got a dinner date with a certain young lady."

"Ah ha! I think I can guess who. You should have seen the way she was looking at you while you were grilling that so-called professor. How about lunch tomorrow then? I only go back to the States at the end of the week."

"You're on," I said. "Which McDonald's are you taking me to?"

"Oh no, they're too expensive! Give me your number and I'll give you a call." We swapped numbers. What would we do without our mobile phones, I thought?

Taleb ambled off to save the world. Either that, or to write some philosophy, or to calculate the black swan unlikelihood of British trains running on time.

Meanwhile, I walked out of the building to be confronted by a barrage of flashing cameras, journalists and even a few TV news teams. They were of course waiting to interview Sarah Richardson after her ordeal. They would decry the near-miss of a travesty of justice and criticise the police and the Crown Prosecution Service for hounding an innocent woman; neatly forgetting that in their same columns or broadcasts, she had, right up to this very morning, been portrayed as a wicked child killer.

It seemed they were also interested in a young member of the jury who had helped bring down the house of cards. I was about to have a (very) brief two days of fame.

Postscript

The above trial is a highly fictional representation of many real arguments used in, and after, two very real landmark trials on cot deaths, with different mothers as defendants, but with the same expert witness. All names are fictional. The actual statistic quoted by the real-life expert, whom we shall call 'Professor A', was 'one in 73 million for two cot deaths', and this led directly or indirectly to guilty verdicts in both trials.

There was extensive media coverage of the first landmark trial. The media originally condemned the defendant, and this can only have negatively influenced the jury. A juror was seen coming into the courtroom on the morning after the Professor's testimony, holding a leading national paper who's frontpage headline was the 'one in 73 million' statistic. The defendant was later found guilty and received a life sentence. Even her first appeal failed before she was later released, after three years in prison, on her second appeal, following another media storm, this time belatedly in her favour.

Both the original trial and the first appeal were considered, afterwards, as travesties of justice. There never was a bright young juror to save the day.

It was only after the original trial that the 'one in 73 million' statistic received criticism from professional statisticians. The Royal Statistical Society issued a press release stating that the figure had indeed 'no statistical basis' and was 'one example of a medical expert making a serious statistical error'. The Society's president later wrote an open letter of complaint to the Lord Chancellor about these concerns.

The statistical criticisms were threefold: first, the 'prosecutor's fallacy', where the unlikely probability of sequential natural deaths was favoured to 'prove guilt' to the detriment of testing the other hypothesis, which is murder, which is deemed even more unlikely; secondly, the 'ecological fallacy' where Professor A assumed the cot death probability within any single family was the same as the aggregate probability for all cot deaths, without taking into account conditions specific to individual families (such as the notion of a S.I.D.S. gene); this latter error was compounded with the notion of assuming 'statistical independence' between events.

The perils of allowing non-statisticians to present unsound statistical arguments were expressed in an editorial in the *British Medical Journal*, pointing out that 'defendants deserve the same protection as patients'.

Furthermore, later research by the defendant's husband into hospital records found that the pathologist had withheld results from blood tests that showed serious bacteriological infection.

For the other, parallel, landmark trial of double cot deaths, several real-life prosecution arguments have also been integrated into this story: the suspicious telephone call to the husband, Professor A's diagnosis of the mother suffering from F.D.I.A., and his rejection of a genetic explanation stating that there was no family history of cot deaths. Only after the trial did more detailed research into family ancestors show several cases of unexplained infant deaths...

All this led to the different appeals where at last both defendants were acquitted.

In the aftermath, several other convictions for unlawful infant death where Professor A had testified were also overturned on appeal.

However, during the three years she served in prison, the mother from the first trial was separated from her third baby (who fortunately had no problems). She suffered abuse from other prisoners because, it was assumed, she was a child killer, on top of being the daughter of a policeman. These combined traumas led the mother to die, unintentionally, from alcohol poisoning a few years later. She never did recover from the ordeal.

Professor A eventually apologised for all his misleading evidence at these various trials. The solicitor general barred him from any further court appearances.

Professor A was found guilty of 'serious professional misconduct' by the General Medical Council and was struck off the medical register. However, and somewhat unbelievably, the Society of Expert Witnesses commented that the severity of this punishment would cause many professionals to reconsider whether to stand as expert witnesses. Professor A later won a High Court appeal against the G.M.C. decision and was reinstated.

Later on, advice was given to all prosecutors to never allow a conviction only on the evidence of an 'expert witness'.

A ruling from the Supreme Court of Queensland was later adopted into English law, that effectively banned the use of F.D.I.A. as an identifiable disease. It could only be used as a *description* of a range behaviours: '*A label used to describe a behaviour is not helpful in determining guilt and is prejudicial.*'

Professor A's ex-wife accused him of 'seeing mothers with F.D.I.A. symptoms wherever he looked'.

Acknowledgements

I have used public documents to understand the statistical and other errors made by the prosecution in the original landmark trials; but any similarities stop there, since this is a work of fiction. The families of those originally concerned have suffered enough, and so have not been involved in this work.

Meanwhile, Nassim Taleb's books are very real, and provide probably the best understanding possible of randomness and uncertain events, as applied to life, finance and even philosophy.

I, like my fictional narrator, also once studied Ocean Engineering with all the mathematical statistical analysis of random waves, so I particularly enjoyed Taleb's books. And I would even thoroughly recommend these books for the Judge Braithwaites of this world (who probably did – just – pass his maths O-level).

I borrowed unashamedly many of Taleb's useful concepts to illustrate the use and misuse of statistics, in particular:

- A lottery winner being accused of cheating due to the improbability of any individual winning.
- Whether you would cross a river that is four feet deep on average.
- Wrongly assuming that random results means random causes.
- The 'silent evidence' bias: people who have died (in infancy in this case) are no longer around to tell you about it.
- Wrongly confusing '*no evidence of...* (disease, or cot death gene)' with '*evidence of no...* (disease, or cot death gene)'.
- Why there is no need to panic if a woman tests positive for a mammography.

Michael Carter
February 2020

The following technical appendices are for those who wish to understand the mathematics behind some of the probability concepts discussed in this book, in particular the 'prosecutor's fallacy'.

Appendix 1

Bayes' Theorem

Bayes' theorem is:

$$P(A \mid B) = P(B \mid A)\, P(A) / P(B)$$

where A and B are events, and $P(B) \neq 0$.

$P(A)$ and $P(B)$ are the probabilities of A and B happening independently of each other.

$P(A \mid B)$ is a conditional probability: the likelihood of A occurring given that B is true.

$P(B \mid A)$ is also a conditional probability: the likelihood of B occurring given that A is true.

How to derive Bayes' theorem from first principals:

$$P(A \mid B) = P(A \cap B) / P(B), \text{ if } P(B) \neq 0$$
$$P(B \mid A) = P(B \cap A) / P(A), \text{ if } P(A) \neq 0$$

where $P(A \cap B)$ is the joint probability of A and B being true.

Since $P(B \cap A) = P(A \cap B)$

$$\rightarrow P(A \cap B) = P(A \mid B) \, P(B) = P(B \mid A) \, P(A)$$

$$\rightarrow P(A \mid B) = P(B \mid A) \, P(A) / P(B), \text{ if } P(B) \neq 0$$

Appendix 2

Application of Bayes' theorem to compare two cot deaths with two murders, and comparison with the 'prosecutor's fallacy'.

Reminder:

$$P(A \mid B) = P(B \mid A) \, P(A) / P(B)$$

Let us call event A 'two cot deaths', represented by 2CD.
And call event B 'two deaths', represented by 2D.

$$P(2CD \mid 2D) = P(2D \mid 2CD) \times P(2CD) / P(2D)$$

Probability of the cause being two cot deaths, given that two deaths have happened = Probability of innocence	= Probability of two deaths given that two cot deaths have happened = 1, since by definition, a cot death is a death	x Probability of two cot deaths on their own	/ Probability of two deaths on their own, whatever the cause

If event 2M is 'two murders'.

Let us now simplify and say that it is either two cot deaths or two murders, then:

$$P(2D) = P(2CD) + P(2M)$$

Then since $P(2D \mid 2CD) = 1$ as explained above

$$P(2CD \mid 2D) = P(2CD) / [P(2CD) + P(2M)]$$
$$= 1 / [1 + P(2M)/P(2CD)]$$

The prosecutor's fallacy is to say that 'the probability of two cot deaths being the cause of the two deaths that have already happened $P(2CD \mid 2D)$ is equal to the probability of two cot deaths independently $P(2CD)$', which this equation shows not to be true.

The real probability is a function of the *ratio* of the probability of two murders to the probability of two cot deaths:

$$1 / [1 + P(2M)/P(2CD)]$$

So, we see that it is not the rarity of the probability of two cot deaths that matters $P(2CD)$, this value alone is irrelevant. Once a rare event of two deaths has actually happened, what counts is the ratio of the probability of the two hypotheses, both rare events.

Different examples
If the probability of two murders were to approach one, that is certainty, (due to other overwhelming evidence to

show it was murder), only then can the prosecutor make this shortcut to stop the defendant claiming it was accidental:

Only if $P(2M) \sim 1$, then:
$$P(2CD \mid 2D) \sim 1 / [1 + 1/P(2CD)]$$
$$\sim P(2CD) / [P(2CD) + 1]$$
$$\sim P(2CD) \text{ since } P(2CD) \ll 1$$

And since $P(2CD)$ can be quite a low value, the probability of innocence is in this case also low.

Let's explore some other simple cases:

If, for example, the probability of two cot deaths was very much larger than the probability of two murders:

$$P(2CD) \gg P(2M)$$

So, the probability of the two deaths being due to two cot deaths is:

$$P(2CD \mid 2D) \sim 1 / 1$$

or almost 100%, i.e. it was certainly accidental, not murder, which makes sense.

If, for example, there was an equal probability of two cot deaths or two murders, then:

$$P(2CD) = P(2M)$$

So, the probability of the two deaths being due to two cot deaths is:

$$P(2CD \mid 2D) = 1 / [1 + 1]$$
$$= \frac{1}{2}$$

or 50%, which also makes sense. But such a high probability of innocence should never lead to a conviction in a court of law.

If, for example, the probability of two accidental cot deaths was three times more likely than the probability of two murders:

$$P(2CD) = 3\ P(2M)$$

So, the probability of the two deaths being due to two accidental cot deaths is:

$$P(2CD \mid 2D) = 1 / [1 + 1/3]$$
$$= 0.75, \text{ or } 75\% \text{ probability of innocence.}$$

Possible scenario for the Richardson family

Let us go back to the Richardson trial in this book. Goodwin himself suggested that one murder was less likely than one cot death. But he also insisted that if the mother suffers from F.D.I.A., then both murders are more likely; similarly, Fielding insists that if there is a cot death gene, both cot deaths are more likely (statistical dependence in both cases).

So, for the sake of argument:

- Let us assume the average probability for a cot death is one in 8,500, while the average probability for infant murder is half (it is doubtless less than this), one in 17,000.

- Let us assume Mrs Richardson has a cot death gene that multiplies the likelihood of cot death by 100, so each cot death has one in 85 chance. So, a double cot death has a one in 7,225 chance.
- To please Professor Goodwin, let us assume Mrs Richardson also suffers from F.D.I.A. that multiplies her risk of murdering her child by the same factor of 100, so each murder now has a one in 170 chance. So, a double murder has a one in 28,900 chance.

In which case the probability of double cot death is 28,900 / 7,225 = 4 times that of double murder (which makes sense, we assumed double the odds for cot death, which with two events becomes $2^2 = 4$ times more likely).

Putting $P(2M)/P(2CD) = 1/4$ in our above equation gives a probability of the two deaths being due to two accidental cot deaths of:

$$P(2CD \mid 2D) = 1 / [1 + 1/4]$$
$$= 0.8 \text{ or } 80\% \text{ chance of innocence.}$$

This sort of a ratio would totally exonerate Mrs Richardson in any court of law.

Impact of other evidence to suggest murder

Now let us analyse a scenario where there is other evidence to suggest Mrs Richardson had indeed committed murder. If we really thought that there was, say, a 50% chance that Mrs Richardson had killed her son or sons, and that this evidence was specific to her, perhaps due to some clearly identified motive, or perhaps due to the fact that she boasted about it afterwards, in this case some of Professor's Goodwin's last minute comments would be valid.

Even if we have the 'best case' (for Mrs Richardson's) gene situation, where the probability of cot death is 1000 times higher than the average, $P(2CD) = 1/72.25 = 0.01384$.

But the stand-alone probability of murder $P(2M)$ has shot right up to 0.5, which is much more than $P(2CD)$, so this will have an important impact on the calculation. The plausible 'alternative murder hypothesis' comes into play:

So, the probability of innocence:

$$P(2CD \mid 2D) = 1 / [1 + P(2M)/P(2CD)]$$
$$= 1 / [1 + 0.5 / 0.01384]$$
$$= 0.02694, \text{ or one out of } 37.$$

This would not look good for Mrs Richardson and would quite possibly get her convicted.

But remember, here we are approaching the evidence from a completely different angle. The other evidence strongly suggests foul play, specific to Mrs Richardson. This is when we look into whether the statistics can provide some proof to exonerate her, or not, with the existence of a natural death hypothesis. In this case, not really.

However, in the scenario of this book, as in the true story, it seems legitimate to say the marks around the mouth could have happened to any family finding itself in a similar situation, thus it is *not specific* to Mrs Richardson (as Fielding points out to Goodwin near the end of the trial), hence you cannot use the 50% probability, or some other percentage, as the $P(2M)$ in the above equations.

Appendix 3

Applying Bayes' theorem to mammograph testing for breast cancer

$P(A \mid B) = P(B \mid A) \, P(A) \, / \, P(B)$

Let us call event A 'has cancer', represented by C.

And let us call event B 'positive mammography result', represented by M+.

$P(C \mid M+) \quad = \quad P(M+ \mid C) \quad x \quad P(C) \quad / \quad P(M+)$

Probability of having cancer given a positive mammography result	= Probability of the mammography giving a positive result if there is a cancer. Assume = 1 (i.e. no false negatives)	x Probability of cancer in the general population	/ Probability of the mammography giving positive result = probability of detecting a cancer + probability of a false positive

If we use USA statistics:

- Every year 38 million women are tested for breast cancer.
- Of these 140,000 have cancer.
- Let's assume the probability of a false positive for a test is 10% (i.e. out of a hundred healthy women without cancer that are tested, the mammography will give an erroneous positive result for ten of them).

So, the probability of getting a positive mammography result:

$$P(M+) = \text{probability of detecting a cancer}$$
$$+ \text{ probability of false positive}$$
$$= [140{,}000 + 10\% \times (38 \text{ million} - 140{,}000)] \, / \, 38 \text{ million}$$
$$= 0.1033$$

$$P(C) = \text{probability of cancer in general population}$$
$$= 140{,}000 \, / \, 38 \text{ million}$$
$$= 0.003684, \text{ or } 0.3684\%$$

$P(M+ \mid C)$ = Probability of the mammography giving a positive result if there is a cancer. Assume this = 1 (i.e. no false negatives)

So, the probability of cancer once a mammography gives a positive result:

$$P(C \mid M+) = P(M+ \mid C) \times P(C) \, / \, P(M+)$$
$$= 1 \times 0.003684 \, / \, 0.1033$$

$$= 0.03566, \text{ or } 3.566\%$$

So due to the false positives, a positive mammography test still only indicates 3.6% chance of cancer. The mammography has served to eliminate 90% of the healthy women. So, a positive result increases the probability of cancer almost ten times from 0.37% for the general population to 3.6%.

Appendix 4

Applying Bayes' theorem to the 'defence attorney's fallacy' in the O.J. Simpson trial

$$P(A \mid B) = P(B \mid A) \, P(A) / P(B)$$

Let us call event A 'woman murdered by her batterer', represented by M,B.

And call event B 'woman murdered', represented by M.

A bit further below we will introduce another event 'a woman battered by her significant other', represented by B.

$$P(M, B \mid M) = P(M \mid M,B) \quad x \quad P(M,B) \quad / \quad P(M)$$

Probability of a woman having been murdered by her batterer once she is found murdered	= Probability of the woman being murdered, once she has been murdered by her batterer = 1 since she has indeed been murdered.	x Probability of a woman being murdered by her batterer.	/ Probability of a woman being murdered overall.

William Skorupski and Howard Wainer, in their paper 'The Bayesian flip: Correcting the prosecutor's fallacy' (Royal Statistical Society, August 2015) use the following data, which they in turn got from the Clark County Prosecuting Attorney webpage and a 2010 *New York Times* article by Steven Strogatz:

- In 1992, the population of women in the USA was approximately 125 million.
- In that year 4,956 women were murdered.
- Approximately 3.5 million of women are battered every year.
- In that same year 1,432 women were murdered by their previous batterers.

The probability of a woman being murdered overall:

P(M) = 4,956 / 125 million
= 0.00003965

The probability of a woman being battered:

P(B) = 3.5 million / 125 million
= 0.028

The probability of a woman being murdered by her batterer in the whole population:

P(M, B) = 1,432 / 125 million
= 0.00001146, or one in 87,290.

The conditional probability of a *still living* woman *subsequently* being murdered by her batterer assuming she was indeed already being battered:

P(M, B | B) = 1,432 / 3.5 million
             = 0.0004091, or one in 2,444.

This is the (approximate) ratio that O.J. Simpson's defence used in his 1994 trial to counter the prosecution's evidence that Simpson beat his ex-wife and their deduction that this significantly increased his chance of having been her murderer. The defence said that since only one out of 2,500 battered women go on to be murdered, the prosecution's evidence was of no relevance to the trial, and so the jury should ignore it.

But we will see that this probability P(M, B | B) is not relevant, in this case the 'defence attorney's fallacy'. As already stated, it is merely the probability of a battered and *still living* woman being subsequently murdered before we find any dead body.

What we need to determine is P(M, B | M), the probability that the woman was murdered by her spouse, given that she has *indeed been found murdered*:

P(M, B | M) = P(M | M, B) x P(M, B) / P(M)

P(M | M, B) is the probability of the woman being murdered, once she has been murdered by her batterer = 1 as already stated.

So:

$$P(M, B \mid M) = 1 \times 0.00001146 / 0.00003965$$
$$= 0.2890, \text{ or a one in } 3.5 \text{ chance,}$$

of a battered and murdered woman, having been murdered by her batterer.

This would have been an important addition to the trial in light of a wealth of other evidence accusing Simpson of the crime.

However, thanks to the defence attorney's fallacy amongst other arguments, Simpson was acquitted.

Appendix 5

The 'ecological factor'

The question 'would you cross a river that is four feet deep *on average?*' comes from Nassim Taleb's *The Black Swan.*

As pointed out both in the main story and in the Postscript, the 'ecological fallacy' is where the Professor assumed the cot death probability within any single family was the same as the aggregate (or average) probability for all cot deaths, without taking into account conditions specific to individual families (such as the notion of a S.I.D.S. gene).

Even without accounting for a hypothetical cot-death gene, Professor A's real-life data showed a lot of variability. The data was extracted from the C.E.S.D.I. study (Confidential Enquiry into Sudden Death in Infancy). This analysed 400 sudden infant deaths in the UK over a period of three years from 1993 to 1995 inclusive. The report identified three main factors associated with an increased risk of death in a particular household, which were (1) the presence of smokers, (2) younger mothers under twenty-seven, and (3) whether the household had no wage earner.

We see an incredible variation depending on which factors are present, ranging from one cot death in 8,543 live births, to one in 214 births:

S.I.D.S rates for different factors based on the data from the C.E.S.D.I. S.U.D.I. Study:

	S.I.D.S. incidence in this group:
Overall rate in the study population	One cot death for each 1,303 live births
Rate for groups with different factors:	
Anybody smokes in the household Nobody smokes in the household	One in 737 One in 5,041
No waged income in the household At least one waged income in the household	One in 486 One in 2,088
Mother less than 27 years old Mother 27 years old or more	One in 567 One in 1,882
None of these factors One of these factors Two of these factors All three of these factors	One in 8,543 One in 1,616 One in 596 One in 214

With this variation in data, it was statistically very dangerous to assume that the one in 8,543 average for the Richardson's type of household applied exactly to the Richardsons.

This is also a fair proof that different environmental factors (amongst others) can influence the incidence of S.I.D.S.:

- Hence cot deaths are not random, even if they appear to be.
- Hence you cannot assume statistical independence by squaring the individual probability to get the probability of two events happening.
- There is statistical dependence: the arrival of one cot death suggests higher odds of a second cot death.

The incidence of a possible cot death gene (not identified in this study) could only accentuate this statistical dependence.

It is interesting to observe the real-life contradictions:

- While the eminent medical Professor A testified in several trials that there was no evidence of increased risk of having a second cot death once a first had happened.
- We found, meanwhile, that the much more intuitive and down-to-earth NHS healthcare workers always imposed strict controls on second babies born into families having previously suffered a cot death, in particular the use of a sleep apnoea alarm and giving CPR lessons to the parents...

No prizes for guessing who got it right.

About the Author

Michael Carter grew up in Norwich, then studied engineering at Cambridge and Ocean Engineering at UCL, before designing and installing offshore oil platforms - just like the story's narrator.

Later he did his own Brexit and moved to France, and after an MBA at INSEAD (top of his class) he spent the rest of his career in senior management positions in electrical multinationals (CEO of Socomec Group and Vice President at Legrand), before retiring in 2018 to go sailing, mountaineering and write thought provoking books.

He lives in Grasse in the South of France, is married, and has three daughters, two dogs and a sailing boat.

Although this is his first novel as a writer, he has honed his writing skills over the years, since managing multinationals takes a lot of bi-lingual skills in communicating new concepts in as interesting a manner as possible.